Contents

Acknowledgements

This book is intendened for teachers, student teachers and parents. It is not an original work and has drawn upon many brilliantly original papers and books in its compilation. I am particularly indebted to three authors, Professor J.M. Tanner, Professor J.Z. Young FRS and Dr Margaret Donaldson, for their books have provided not only a sound base of fact about growth and the development of the mind/brain but also a supply of fertile ideas. I am especially grateful to Professor Young for his encouragement and for writing the Introduction.

At the end of the book I have made a list of some of the books and papers I have referred to and I have numbered these references in the text, so that a reader can delve more deeply if he or she so wishes. In emphasizing the importance of human variety and potential throughout the book I have stressed the resilience of the human brain and its uniqueness from person to person. Besides these facts I have ventured to say that even in such a short time as the last 50 years, enormous strides have been made in schooling, in the understanding of children's minds and in their health. We have much to be thankful for.

I would like to thank a number of people for reading and commenting critically upon the draft and for their wise counsel and advice not only directly but by correspondence and discussion. They include the following:

Mr. P. Burns, lately HMI Divisional Inspector, South West;

Dr A.C. Fairburn, Consultant Child Psychiatrist, Wiltshire Area Health Authority;

Dr M. Parkinson, Area Specialist (Child Health), Gloucestershire Area Health Authority;

Dr M. Pepper, Medical Officer, DHSS;

Prof. J.R.T. Colley, Prof. of Community Health Bristol University, for reading Chapters 3 and 4;

Prof. W.A. Marshall, Dept. of Human Sciences, Loughborough University, for reading Chapters 6, 13, 15, 16 and 17;

Dr. F. Newcombe, Neuro-psychology Unit, Churchill Hospital, Oxford, for reading Chapters 7, 8, 9 and 12.

Dr. Kenneth Hutton for reading the proofs and for useful comment.

Above all, I wish I could find a new way of thanking Ann who helped most of all

Many of the comments and constructive criticisms made by these readers have been incorporated into the final text but needless to say any errors of fact and judgement that remain are my own.

June 1980   JOHN BRIERLEY

Introduction

There are many books that cover different parts of the sequence of child development but few that follow it all. To do so requires a firm conception of human values, possibilities and also limitations. Dr Brierley has such a view and his deep practical and theoretical knowledge of all aspects of child development is here made available for every parent and teacher. This book will help anyone who has to deal in any way with schools and children. It tells us the facts about all the stages of development from before birth to after adolesence. You can find the statistics on anything from smoking during pregnancy, disruption in the classroom to meeting the needs of gifted pupils. Yet it is a very readable book. On every page there are quotations and anecdotes to lighten the way. Dr Brierley allows all of us to take advantage of his high intellectual quality and wisdom.

J.Z. Young

Chapter 1
History and Perspectives

No work on child development would be complete without a backward glance over the last century, simply to underline how far we have progressed in education, in child health and in the understanding of the growth of a child's mind, in such a relatively short span of time. True, teachers, buildings, education, medicine and social conditions do not change overnight but taking a long view of human development, the hundred years since 1870 — when free elementary education became compulsory and extended the provision made by voluntary effort — is only the last few words in the book of human evolution. Children are larger and healthier at all ages now than then and though we have far to go, more account is taken of the individuality of their bodies and minds in the schools of today than a century or even half a century ago.

Schools now

To indicate progress in schooling, despite some bad patches now and in the past, there has been a substantial advance towards Dr Johnson's definition of education — the formation of manners in youth. Most primary schools as described by HMI in *Primary Education in England*[1] are 'civilized communities', that is, communities in which teachers provide planned opportunities for children to take responsibility and to participate as members of a group or team. Consideration for other people and concern for the natural environment are widely encouraged. Children are expected to take care of materials, equipment and the school generally. In the teaching of reading, writing and mathematics there is a clear priority to bring children up to a minimal level but once the basic techniques are mastered little attention is given to their use and extension. Nevertheless many of these schools are like the three described in the Plowden Report.[2]. In the first of these (an infant school) a visitor would discover in the playground:

> . . . a group of children, with their teacher, clustered round a large square box full of earth. The excitement is all about an earthworm, which none of the children had ever seen before. Their classroom door opens on to the playground and inside are the rest of the class, seated at tables disposed informally about the room, some reading books that they have themselves chosen from the copious shelves along the side of the room and some measuring the quantities of water that different vessels will hold.

In the second school — a junior mixed one — fourth year children were to be found broadcasting poems of their choice through a homemade microphone, while at the third school:

> . . . all the children in the first class were either on top of the church tower or standing in the churchyard and staring intently upwards. The headmaster appeared in the porch and explained what was happening. The children were making a study of the trees in the private park which lay 100 yards beyond the church. The tower party had taken up with them the seeds of various trees and were releasing these on the leeward side, and were measuring the wind speed with a homemade anemometer.

References to more modern examples of good practice taken from the Primary Survey will be found in Chapter 14 and elsewhere.

In *Ten Good Schools*[3] good practice in secondary schools is described in detail; it stresses the importance of good relationships.

> In the much larger schools it is not possible for the heads to know every child but they take great pains to establish structures of co-operation and discipline that foster good relationships. The headmaster of the comprehensive in the educational priority area emphasised that true mutual respect and consideration for others, in a sympathetic and well-ordered community, were the only basis for good relationships: merely to emphasise conformity with superficial standards of dress and speech would be to court rejection of them (as adult and

middle class) by young people in that environment. In every example, discipline appears to be natural, and mutual respect is revealed in the casual courtesies of adults and pupils meeting in corridors as well as in good order in classrooms. The young people respond to the efforts of the staff and take advantage of the many opportunities offered to them in and out of school. In the large comprehensive in an industrial setting, the headmaster said, 'Discipline is often old-fashioned as well as modern. Respect is sought, individuals are treated as such, but all misdeeds are punished. Staff and pupils know exactly the context in which they work, what is expected and what are the limits. The aim is to be the wise and sympathetic parent who does not shrink from what has to be done'. This combination of firmness and understanding appears to have its effect in time: in another school one fourth form which previously had had a very bad record of truancy, aggravated by parental non-cooperation, achieved a steadier attendance.

This description taken from *Ten Good Schools*[3] is confirmed by the recent report, *Aspects of Secondary Education in England*[4] based on the inspection of some 384 secondary schools. Of these the report states:

The great majority are orderly communities where much thought and effort is given to promoting the well-being of individual pupils. Only a very small minority of schools felt themselves to be facing serious behaviour problems. All are anxious to secure basic skills and to enable their pupils to obtain examination qualifications which may be important to their future. They are sensitive to public expectations and aware of the need to prepare their pupils for the responsibilities of adult life.

A look back

If we glance backwards now to the turn of the century things were very different and as Miss S. J. Browne HMI [5], Senior Chief Inspector wrote about the Secondary Survey just mentioned '. . . although there are inevitably things which could be better, the reader in good faith will find much to be grateful for'. In about 1900 a five year old starting school sat at his desk on his first day and he was taught and set tasks and kept there. H. E. Dent[6] records this memory from 1904:

> I was a pre-adolescent pupil in an elementary school in 1904. Like millions more, I intoned my way monotonously (and uncomprehendingly) through the multiplication tables; I was bored to nausea by the one and only 'Reader' we were allowed each year — which had to serve the dual function of giving us practice in the mechanics of reading aloud (why aloud?) and of being our introduction to English life and letters. I wrote, endlessly, in 'copy-books' morally elevating maxims — 'A stitch in time saves nine', 'Too many cooks spoil the broth' — but I never composed, much less wrote, in class a single original sentence. I memorised, in rhyme, the names and idiosyncrasies of the English kings and queens:
>
> > William the Conqueror long did reign,
> > William his son by an arrow was slain . . .
>
> and I memorised (though not in rhyme) the names of the capes, bays, county towns, mountains and rivers, literally all round Britain. And once each week I painted blobs (we called them flowers), and wove wet reeds into work baskets: the school's sole concessions to 'activity'.
>
> Not much in all that 'to form and strengthen the character', or 'develop the intelligence', or 'make the best use of the school years', or fit children, either 'practically' or 'intellectually', 'for the work of life'. And this experience of mine, I must emphasise, was not in the class of a cynical, dull or apathetic teacher, but a lively, intelligent, warm-hearted woman, who as a person did us boys and girls a world of good. Did she know no other way to teach? Or was she bound by the school timetable? — that sacrosanct nineteenth-century visual aid, put up 'in a prominent position' (as the Code required) by the new head teacher when he arrived, and never taken down until he left, it might well be thirty years later. (Men did not move then as they do now. Nor did women, for that matter; the age of the 'dedicated spinster' was just beginning, as one LEA after another refused to employ married women).
>
> Such teaching as I endured went on for many years in many schools after 1904.

Edmond Holmes[7], a former Senior Chief Inspector at the Board of

Education at the turn of the century confirms H. C. Dent's description:

> The one end and aim of the teacher is to do everything for the child; — to feed him with semi-digested food: to hold him by the hand, or rather by both shoulders, when he tries to walk or run; to keep him under close and constant supervision; to tell him in precise detail what he is to think, to feel, to say, to wish, to do; to show him in precise detail how he is to do whatever may have to be done; to lay thin veneers of information on the surface of his mind; never to allow him a minute for independent study; never to trust him with a handbook, a note-book, or a sketch-book; in fine, to do all that lies in his power to prevent the child from doing anything whatever for himself. The result is that the various vital faculties which education might be supposed to train become irretrievably starved and stunted in the over-education school child; till at last, when the time comes for him to leave school in which he has been so sedulously cared for, he is too often thrown out upon the world, helpless, listless, resourceless, without a single interest, without a single purpose in life.

It might be added here as a counterpoise to these assessments that many teachers in those days and indeed in more recent times in the 1930s showed great skill with big classes, encouraging the children to work and be interested. Some in the 1930s were starting to break away from instruction and set work to encourage more initiative and resourcefulness in the children, the fruits of which we see in primary and secondary schools now. It is rewarding in this context to read *The Primary School*.[8] Though half a century has passed in considering the curriculum the report strikes a modern note. 'The essential point is that the curriculum should not be loaded with inert ideas and crude blocks of fact which are devoid of significance till related to some interest in the minds of the pupils. It must be vivid, realistic, a stream in motion, not a stagnant pool.'

Developments in health

Progress in education and health go hand in hand, for a sick, tired and hungry child will not learn properly. To indicate the progression of children towards healthy adults, a look over our shoulder to the conditions in which many of our grandparents and great

grandparents were brought up at schools and at work is instructive —
and humbling.

Charles Robert,[9] a factory doctor writing in 1876 said: 'a factory
child of the present day at the age of nine years weighs as much as one
of ten years did in 1833 . . . each age has gained one year in forty'

In 1833, working boys aged 10 years were on average 121 cm in
height compared with 140 cm today; those aged 18 averaged 160 cm
compared with 175 cm today. From 1900 to 1940 the trend in growth
was about one cm/decade in 12 year olds: from 1950 to 1970 it was
five cm/decade. In industrialized countries like ours the trend is
slowing down.

Statistics are cold though instructive and a snapshot picture[9] of a
Lancashire factory girl of 14 in about 1900 will allow mental
comparisons with most 14 year old girls now.

> The girls exhibit the same shortness of stature, the same
> miserable development, and they possess the same sallow
> cheeks and carious teeth. I have also observed that at an age
> when girls brought up under wholesome conditions usually
> possess a luxuriant growth of hair, these factory girls have a
> scanty crop which, when tied back, is simply a wisp or 'rat's tail'.

The growth of children is described in detail later in this book but it
is worth mentioning now that growth in height is a good measure of
health and is remarkably sensitive not only to nutrition and disease
but to many other influences, including the loving quality of the
home, which play on a child year by year.

Towards the turn of the century there were improvements. Here is
a thumbnail sketch of the improvements in children between 1880
and 1900 described by a headmaster of a Board School in East
London.[10]

> The boy of 1900 as compared with the boy of 1880: Much more
> docile; insubordinate, then endemic, now almost unknown,
> and if it occurs very likely to be the fault of the teacher. Cheerful
> and eager now, then often sullen and morose. Relations with
> teachers generally friendly, often affectionate — no street-
> calling after them or stone throwing as there used to be. All this,
> the result of discipline and control at school, reacts beneficially
> at home. Truancy almost extinct, and when occurring there is
> usually something in the blood to explain it. Theft rather

common, but perhaps more often detected owing to better supervision.

Personal cleanliness: Greatly improved, verminous cases among boys rare, but among girls almost universal. Out of thirty examined, twenty-eight required attention. As to dirt, it is necessary to distinguish between recent dirt got at play and the ancient kind that gives the strong smell. Swimming is taught and has a good effect. The really dirty, seen when stripped, would not be allowed to bathe, but would be sent home to wash there at first. This now seldom happens. The vermin referred to are lice; bugs are rarely seen; but fleas are common, especially on children coming from homes where there is a baby.

Obscene language: Common both in the street and in the home, but not common in the school where, if disagreeable words are heard, they are checked.

Obscene conduct: Very rare. As to boys and girls, the latter are the aggressors.

To move from the sharp detail to the broad statistical front, deaths of children during the first year of life in the early part of this century in England and Wales were 138 per 1,000 babies born alive. In 1979 it was 12 in a thousand. At the turn of the century nearly one out of three child deaths of children between birth and 15 was caused by infectious disease. Today the proportion is less than one out of 30. In 1900[11] over 10,000 children under 15 died from whooping cough, half of them under one year old; seven under-fives died in 1977. Diphtheria, a dreaded and deadly disease took nearly 10,000 childrens' lives in 1900, over half in the first year of life, but caused no deaths of under-fives in 1977. And measles with associated complications in 1900 took almost 13,000 lives most of them under five. In 1977 eight children under five died from the disease and its complications. Spit and coat-sleeve used for cleaning slates helped to spread measles, whooping cough and other diseases at the turn of the century.[12]

Interesting comments on the health of school children came after 1907 when LEAs were obliged by law to have school doctors. When school leavers were medically examined during the period 1913-15, 1 in 10 was found to be malnourished, about five in every 100 had heart disease, nearly three-quarters had some bad teeth. In some schools half the children had verminous heads. Most doctors engaged in medical inspections remember cases when the whole head seemed to be alive with vermin.

Today the nutrition of children has greatly improved. Better economic conditions with a higher standard of living for most people, school dinners, knowledge of food values and health education, have all contributed to the well-being of children. Indeed the dramatic improvement in child mortality over the past century and in the physical health of children was due largely to improved nutrition which would have helped to ward off the number of deaths from all or nearly all the common infections. It is quite likely too that up to the beginning of the twentieth century, infanticide and starvation of children were not uncommon. From the second half of the nineteenth century up to 1939, the advances in nutrition were strongly supported by a reduction in exposure to infection which stemmed directly from supplies of clean, safe drinking water, milk and food, the change from woollen to boilable cotton clothes, the break-up of overcrowded slums and small more spaced-out families.[13]

Not only was the death rate of children lowered by these developments but the death rate of women after childbirth dropped in England and Wales during the last century. The reasons were largely due to the understanding of germs and the need for cleaniness and ventilation in the labour ward.

The improved cleanliness of food has led to great advances in child health. To take milk as an example, here is a report of 1900 (see endnote 9):

> There is reason to believe that Finsbury milk and milk generally in London contains great bacterial contamination. Four unpreserved samples of milk, selected from two good class and two poor class milk shops, gave an average of 2,370,000 bacteria per cubic centimetre, which is about 2,000,000 bacteria in excess of what should be present in good fresh milk. Of 25 milks examined in Finsbury in 1903, 32 per cent contained pus and 40 per cent contained dirt.

Despite the Arcadian scenes depicted by Constable and Morland, the death rates of children were as high in the past in rural areas as in the towns and cities, no doubt because of squalid cottages and contaminated water and milk supplied. In blunt terms, improvement in the health of children and their parents, at least up to the start of World War II, was largely due to better food, improving social conditions and simple cleanliness and not to medical advance.

Since 1939 big changes have come about from a variety of specific measures such as immunization or new, effective treatments. Other improvements have resulted from higher standards of medical care and an appreciation of the educational role of these services in the care of mother and child.

Earlier in this chapter the health and social problems of children and their families around the turn of the century were referred to. Lowndes, G.A.N. (op.cit.) has described the scene in South London on a hot Sunday evening where at every window tired and untidy bored people, old and young, stood or sat, listlessly watching the passing traffic. By the mid-1930s the weekend exodus of young people hiking or cycling had begun. Now the hush of the Victorian Sunday is a thing of the past and needs no description.

Room for improvement

There is no room, however, for complacency; grossly bad conditions for child rearing still exist in England and Wales, for as one kind of hazard is overcome others arise. While infant mortality rates have declined dramatically and go on improving on 1978 figures, we still lag behind other countries, lying eleventh out of 17 for infant mortality and ninth for perinatal mortality (still births and deaths under one week).[14] And the average figure for 1979 of 12 deaths per thousand babies in England and Wales in the first year of life covers up black spots. In Lambeth the rate is 21 per 1,000, but a few miles away and a few steps up the social scale in Bromley it is 12 per 1,000. In Bradford it is 25; Tameside 29; but in Oxfordshire 10 and Bedfordshire 9 per 1,000. Infant mortality is a delicate gauge which sums up living standards but these affect not only mortality but also the growth and development of children. Overcrowding, bad housing, ignorant mothers who do not bother to keep their antenatal appointments, lack of a proper place to store food leading to food poisoning and gastroenteritis are all reflected in the index of infant and perinatal mortality.

Of the infants who survive what the Court Report called the 'holocaust' of infant mortality many will carry into childhood and adult life a significant disability. Better physical health however enables increasing attention to be given to children's behavioural and emotional problems, to personal relationships, to language and speech disorders, to physical disabilities and to the social circumstances of children (e.g. the three-quarter million one-parent families and their special stresses and needs). Attention is also being directed to the preventive role of the health and education services in combating adult disease — of heart and lungs — and in the prevention of accidents in the home and on the roads.

A superficial knowledge of the social and health conditions of the past hundred years is essential not only in order to understand children who were taught in the mass of elementary schools by thousands of dedicated teachers who did their best with huge classes, and with minor equipment and books but to appreciate how far we have come in a relatively short time. We have indeed much to be thankful for.

Learning

Half a century ago, not much thought was given by the mass of teachers as to how children learn. Nevertheless perceptive teachers such as Margaret McMillan and Dr Montessori in the early years of this century and, later, Susan Isaacs[15] in the 1930s, recognized the need to give children more mobility, to allow more self-activity ('it is the children's activity that is the key to their full development') to teach more by arousing their interest in the process of inquiry rather than by telling them just the 'facts' — although of course deliberate instruction was not to be neglected and has an important place in human development. Play by children contributes vitally to development and to later performance and happiness as an adult. Much still has to be discovered about play and its importance in learning. But it is a fact that children especially in the years before adolescence have a strong biological urge to play and they learn much more from playing (as older children and students do from 'guided exploration') than was once recognized. Recently John Holt[16],[17] has pointed out that a large proportion of children not only fail to respond to a regime of continual testing and giving good marks as rewards and low marks as punishments, but display bored rejection and fear of being found wanting.

It is also important in relation to learning to note three special marks of mankind to which major parts of this book will be devoted: man's long childhood, his flexible, 'open' mind and his individuality.

Man's long childhood, the 12 or 13 years before the spurt in growth during adolescence changes a child into a young adult, is a crucially important time for physical, emotional and intellectual development. The mind is now considered to be resilient and not the fixed 'blank slate' of John Locke or 'little vessels' of the Victorians . . . 'ready to have imperial gallons of facts poured into them until they are full to the brim'. This 'filling up' may have derived from the Protestant emphasis on preparation for the future, but modern views have suggested that the mind may have some of the qualities of the elastic surface, easily deformed but able to rebound when those forces are removed and in fact to recover from early disadvantage. As a child grows and develops through his long childhood, he acquires the human marks of speech, thought, self consciousness, reflection and morality. He develops these human attributes because his brain is open and flexible, that is the genetic instructions for his behaviour are only lightly sketched in compared with other animals; but to develop well and to learn innumerable things he needs constant interaction with his environment, with children and with adults.

Finally his individuality of body and mind and the unique way he develops makes it important and *just* to treat each child differently according to his or her individual characteristics at a given age so long as each one is treated as well as possible.

There are still many questions to be answered about child development including the growth of the mind and the way it works but we have made strides in the last century towards that understanding. As Niko Tinbergen,[18] the Nobel Laureate, wrote recently, many advantages might accrue if teachers and parents were to follow closely what the young, emerging science of child development is beginning to discover.

Chapter 2
Individuality and its Origins

Individuality (and therefore variety) is one of the major characteristics of people — in shape, walk, thoughts, intelligence, emotions, actions and so on. It is of course a truism that *likenesses* in looks or character, for instance, are passed on in families, sometimes skipping a generation. 'He has his father's eyes' or 'his mother's good temper' or 'his grandfather's quickness at figures' are common enough sayings in families but even so each child is 'himself', not exactly like his brothers and sisters or his parents. George Eliot in *Adam Bede* made these remarks about heredity:

> Family likeness has often a deep sadness in it. Nature, that great tragic dramatist, knits us together by bone and muscle, and divides us by the subtler web of our brains; blends yearning and repulsion; and ties us by our heart-strings to the beings that jar us at every movement. We hear a voice with the very cadence of our own uttering the thoughts we despise; we see eyes — ah, so like our mother's — averted from us in cold alienation; and our last darling child startles us with the air and gestures of the sister we parted from in bitterness long years ago. The father to whom we owe our best heritage — the mechanical instinct, the keen sensibility to harmony, the unconscious skill of the modelling hand — galls us and puts us to shame by his daily errors; the long-lost mother, whose face we begin to see in the glass as our own wrinkles come, once fretted our young souls with her anxious humours and irrational persistence.

Likenesses and differences

Similarities are easy enough to understand but it is not quite so easy to understand the *differences,* slight or large, between family members.[19] A child often has the 'family face' but his own version of it. Sometimes he bears little resemblance to his brothers and sisters. He may be exceptionally bright or, sadly, handicapped in some way or perhaps he may be a startling red-head. Variety among children in a family is commonplace. Every teacher with a class of children in front of him bears witness to it daily. In a group of 14 year old boys puberty has started in one but not in another: one is a man in body already, the rest still boys. Amongst five year olds, one has excellent hand control and uses scissors to cut out skilfully, another is clumsy; one has a large vocabulary on entering school but another of the same age a meagre one. One child starts school at five and on her first day stands and watches shyly while another goes to play at once.

The explanation of these likenesses and differences between people in character and intelligence, whether they are related or not, is not an easy one. Broadly speaking characteristics are divided into those that are hereditary or genetic on the one hand and those that are due to the environment on the other. This is not a simple, clear-cut matter because heredity and environment interact in the production of each and every character and we cannot say how much has been contributed by each to most human characteristics. A few characters are unaffected by the environment: the blood group or finger-print pattern for instance. The most important human attributes and all those that are the concern of this book — height, weight, skin-fold thickness, 'intelligence', indices of mental stability, emotion — are the product of the heredity/environment interaction. The proportion of the inherited to the environmental component is unique to each individual. Put in another and more practical way, the family and school environments are crucial in determining which and how much of the potential inherited from parents is fulfilled.

Just how difficult it is to unravel which characteristics are due to heredity and which to environment is shown by a study of the causes of weight variation in babies at birth.[20] Thirty per cent of the variation is due to unknown causes — perhaps the position of the foetus. The rest have been categorized thus: the influence of the hereditary constitution of the mother (20 per cent); of the child (16 per cent); the sex of the child (2 per cent). Environmental influences: 24 per cent of the weight variation is due to the mother's health and nutrition; 7 per cent to the order of the baby's birth; 1 per cent to the mother's age.

Heredity

Basic information on the working of heredity is now well-known (see Brierley, op.cit.). The bringing together of hereditary material is ensured by having two different kinds of reproductive cells (gametes), a relatively large passive egg and a small active sperm which fuse at fertilization. The human egg can just be seen by the naked eye and is slightly smaller than the stop at the end of this sentence (140 μm in diameter). The sperm is scarcely 10 μm across and 100 μm long. After fertilization the zygote (fertilized egg) weighs about 34 thousandths of a gramme.

The normal human sperm and egg each contain 23 chromosomes and these form the genetic dowry of the child. The chromosomes themselves are microscopic, threadlike bodies each of which carries a code for the future development of the individual. The code is contained in units (genes) which are too small to be detected by the microscope. These remarkable gene units which number probably 10^4 or 10^5 on the 23 pairs of chromosomes contain the chemical instructions for the design and development of the foetus provided the right 'environment' is present in the uterus in the shape of proper food and oxygen for growth.

The fertilized egg (zygote), then, has 46 chromosomes in 23 pairs. One of each pair has been obtained from the father through the sperm and the other from the mother through the egg. Forty four of these chromosomes can be seen under the microscope to be in matching pairs. In a boy there is a discrepancy in the twenty-third pair. One chromosome of this pair is much smaller than the other and is known as the Y or male sex chromosome. It is in fact the male determiner. On its presence or absence depends whether a boy or girl baby is born. The Y's partner is the X chromosome. A boy baby has 22 matching pairs of chromosomes and an odd pair XY. A girl has no such odd pair and has 23 pairs of matching chromosomes of which one pair is the XX pair.

The sex of the child is settled in the first half-hour of life. There is nothing mysterious about this for gender is determined by the father's sperm. Half a man's sperm cells carry a Y chromosome and half an X. If a Y carrying sperm fuses with an egg, an XY zygote is formed which eventually develops into a boy. The XX zygote develops into a girl.

The boy/girl difference is perhaps the most basic kind of human variety. Other variations within a family come about because the genetic blueprint of the child is often slightly different from that of each parent because the egg and sperm from which a child is formed each carries a different arrangement of genes from each of the parental sets. This is because the units of heredity, the genes, can be combined and recombined in different ways during egg and sperm formation so that, although all the genes in a child may well be identical to those of his parents, they may as indicated be shuffled into a slightly different order on the chromosomes and so have a slightly different effect in the off-spring.

Rarely, a gene may be quite different from that of the parent because its chemical nature has changed through mutation. A mutation can help to make us differ from our parents, however slightly. Sometimes an extra chromosome gets caught up in the fertilized egg to make a package of 47 rather than the normal 46. In some cases this causes Down's syndrome, commonly called 'mongolism'. This is not a good term because there is no relationship between the appearance of the abnormality and members of the Mongolian race, although superficially they look like them in the fold of the eyelid. As will now be clear, each one of us has been formed by a kind of genetic lottery. It made Aldous Huxley write:

> A million, million spermatozoa,
> All of them alive;
> Out of their cataclysm but one poor Noah
> Dare hope to survive.
> And among that billion minus one
> Might have chanced to be
> Shakespeare, another Newton, a new Donne —
> But the One was Me.

It is an amazing thought that a child with all its attributes develops from the tiny fertilized egg weighing only a fraction of a milligramme.

When the fertilized egg in the uterus begins to divide into two, four, eight, sixteen cells, each cell contains the set of 46 chromosomes. From the time of fertilization up to the end of the eighth week the mass of cells which will become the baby is technically called the embryo; from the ninth week to birth it is called a foetus.

When a baby is born it has about 25 million million cells all of which are identical in chromosome number, exactly duplicating the genetic information in the original fertilized egg.

The uniqueness of the individual

One might ask why the maintenance of human variety is essential. Variety of people in a society not only adds delight and interest to the human scene but is of great importance since it makes the human species more adaptable to change. The hereditary machinery as explained makes variety possible by dealing out different packages of genes to each individual. It has been estimated that each human parent is potentially capable of producing over eight million genetically unique types of gamete.

The unique character of each child can sometimes make it very hard for parents to value and love him for himself whatever his attributes. Children need more than anything to be accepted and rejoiced over, whoever and whatever they are. For teachers it can be equally hard because some children are downright nasty and unlikeable even at five. But for each and every one, success needs to be found and praise and encouragement need to be given — 'we get interested in what we get good at' — to quote Jerome Bruner's[21] simple truth. Human variety suggests an important principle for education: equal treatment for all is not fair treatment for all. 'Discovery' methods for instance thoughtlessly applied to all children in a class may put some at grave disadvantage since some shy, introverted children like rules to work to while extroverted children do better by having explanations of 'rules' after practical, discovery methods.

On a more general plane, to make the most of individual abilities each child because of his or her different (not 'better') hereditary endowment needs a different environment to develop his or her talents to the utmost. This is a far-off goal but it is one worth striving for. Many primary schools adopt a variety of types of organization in arranging the work of the classes. The report on *Primary Education in England* states that in the mass of schools the organization is designed 'to provide satisfactorily for children of different attainments and abilities, to accommodate various types of work, including practical work, and to take advantage of the resources and teaching strength available within a particular school'. Most secondary schools attempt to give educational justice to children: some by streaming, grouping or setting in groups of roughly similar abilities, others by 'mixed ability' teaching. Whatever system is used it follows from a knowledge of human variation that it is just to treat different children differently so long as each is treated as well as possible.

Chapter 3

Some Origins of Abnormality

The great majority of babies are born normal and healthy but substantial malformations are evident in two out of every 100 born live or stillborn. These suffer from congenital abnormalities which arise before birth and might seriously interfere with the everyday life of the affected child if it lived. The defects involve heart ailments, cleft lips and palates, malformations of the bones and joints, Down's syndrome, spina bifida and many others.

To gloss this statement with the facts,[22] in England and Wales the March quarter of 1979, 200.2/10,000 live and still births were malformed. Malformations of the limbs had a rate of 83/10,000, 27/10,000 were of the central nervous system, 12/10,000 of the heart, about the same for cleft lip and/or cleft palate and about 8/10,000 were chromosome defects. Some affected babies die soon after birth but when all surviving children are carefully assessed, surveys have shown that about four in 1,000[23] are or will in infancy become severely mentally handicapped. As children grow up other disorders reveal themselves. Among top junior children in a prosperous area of England a prevalence of one handicapped pupil in every seven was found. Of four handicapping conditions the majority were educationally backward, next came psychiatric disorders, then physically handicapped children and finally those with intellectual retardation. Mild conditions were not recorded (see Court Report).

Advances in medicine and surgery are taking place so that at least some of these defects can be corrected before five and a child can start school in normal or improved health and confidence. Heart surgery is one field of major advance. Nevertheless a child who is seriously or even mildly handicapped physically or mentally makes great emotional and physical demands on parents and indeed on the whole family and on his teachers. For those children who understand their own condition (and they are many) demands on personal courage and character are very great.

Important questions are: how do these abnormalities arise and can they be prevented?

Hereditary hazards

Abnormal development is the result of the interaction between heredity and environmental conditions in the uterus. The comparative importance of these factors varies but about 75 per cent of abnormalities are the result of the complex and subtle interaction of heredity and environment which is very difficult to untangle. About 25 per cent are clear-cut caused directly by faults in either heredity or environment. They include certain types of of subnormal intelligence which have a very simple, clear-cut hereditary basis.[24] Sufferers from Down's syndrome have considerable impairment of intellectual functioning. These unfortunate children have an extra chromosome which reduces intelligence (and brain size) and affects development, personality and behaviour. Phenylketonuria is another abnormality of body chemistry based on the inheritance of a single gene in double dose, one from the mother, the other from the father. Both parents are healthy and normal but the unfortunate baby, unless its defect is detected (which it can be), will be harmed in mental function, a condition thought to be due to abnormal chemical substances accumulating in the tissues. Fortunately phenylketonuriac children can be helped by special diets. Both Down's syndrome and phenylketonuria are totally hereditary in origin.

There are few hard facts to report on the prevention of congenital abnormalities but it is well known that the frequency of Down's syndrome in a baby is 0.7 per 1,000 live births for mothers under 30 and 3 per 1,000 for mothers over 30[25]. It seems, on this evidence, as if the mechanism for the exact division of the chromosomes in reproduction wears out with age but this is not yet proved. It is important to point out too that the *majority* of abnormalities are screened out naturally during the first three months of pregnancy, by natural abortion. This is part of a bigger puzzle: why only about 30 per cent of human conceptions ever survive to birth with the rest including most abnormalities becoming what is called 'foetal wastage'.

A speculation on the causes of these congenital abnormalities is that fertilization of an egg by dying sperms or of a dying egg by a normal sperm may be responsible for genetic abnormality. A sperm remains active for one or two days and eggs for between six and 24 hours and perhaps the capacity for 'healthy' fertilization declines suddenly, but this is not known. It seems clear that frequent coitus in the middle of the reproductive cycle when the egg is released is the way to beget healthy children[26].

Sometimes the environment of the uterus is the major contributor to abnormality. The rapidly growing foetus is especially vulnerable to infections such as German measles; also to nicotine and carbon monoxide poisoning from cigarettes; to drugs, to excess alcohol to vitamin deficiencies and to chronic malnutrition, hazards which in most cases are avoidable.

Smoking and birth weight

The greatest precaution a couple can take to ensure the best outcome of the mother's pregnancy is to stop smoking for the whole nine month period of pregnancy. Mothers who smoke have babies which are on average about 200 g (just under $1/2$ lb) lighter than those born to mothers who do not smoke. It has been estimated that in a pregnancy of normal duration the decrease in birth weight would be eight to nine g for each cigarette smoked daily (i.e. smoking 10 cigarettes a day is associated with a birth weight reduction of 80-90 g per day). In one large British study by Prof. Neville Butler[27] it was shown that $5^{1}/_{2}$ per cent of the babies born to non-smoking mothers were less than 2.5 kg in weight (low birth weight) compared to almost double that percentage for mothers who smoke. Prof. Butler also calculated that some 1,500 babies are still-born in Britain every year as a direct result of mother's smoking. Husbands should also stop smoking because their smoke may be passed on to the unborn baby from a smoke-filled room. What precise factors in the process of smoking cause retarded growth of the baby in the uterus are not known but carbon monoxide is under suspicion. Carbon monoxide from the mother's circulation is taken up and possibly concentrated in the baby's blood. Because CO displaces oxygen in the blood, smoking reduces the amount of oxygen available to the baby's growing tissues, and slows growth.

There is other evidence too that the children born to a mother who smoked 10 or more cigarettes a day (heavy smokers) throughout pregnancy are at the age of seven shorter by about half a centimetre than the children of non-smoking mothers and are retarded in their reading, mathematics and general ability by about four months (Davies, R., Butler, N. and Goldstein, H., op.cit.)[27]. It is possible, but not proven, that smoking during pregnancy reduces the number of cells in a baby's brain.

Parental smoking may be associated with increased risk that their children will develop respiratory disease — bronchitis and pneumonia — in the first year of life. Damage to health is therefore due also to the continued attack by environmental tobacco smoke and not simply due to pre-natal influence alone.

After allowing for associated social and biological factors, therefore, smoking in pregnancy seems to have a persisting adverse effect on the growth and development of seven year olds and even upon 11 year olds. It is possible of course that the life-style of a smoking mother may not be conducive to good growth or to stimulating good reading habits in children. Perhaps with regard to reading, less emphasis is placed on academic achievements in a household of smokers. But the weight of evidence points to the hazards of smoking in pregnancy.

Malnutrition

As well as smoking, *chronic* malnutrition throughout pregnancy (more common in the Third World than here) can result in a baby having a lower birth weight and smaller brain than average and of course such a child could be backward. Although short periods of malnutrition or inadequate diet during pregnancy may not harm the baby it is vital for a mother to eat properly for the greater part of the time. As pointed out earlier a significant number of British babies are born with a low birth weight. They are victims of slow growth in the womb at the very time which is crucial for proper brain development.

A good diet including fresh leafy vegetables, fruit and wholemeal bread, as is well known, contains essential vitamins. It has been known for 30 years that deficiency of a B vitamin, folic acid, causes malformations of the central nervous system of animals. This and other vitamins — A, B^2 and C — have been found to be present in lower quantities in the blood of women on low incomes where spina bifida and anencephaly is three times more common than those who are better off.

These vitamins are essential for the normal growth and division of cells. During the first few weeks following conception the foetus grows rapidly and one of the first distinct parts to be formed is the spinal cord and brain as Chapter 4 describes.

If this growth is interrupted the spinal column will not form properly. Then, if the spinal tube does not close properly at the top end, the brain is not formed — this is anencephaly. If the tube is not formed properly at the bottom end then the spine is left exposed — and this is spina bifida. Together, they are called 'neural tube' defects.

The high frequency of neural tube defects among Celts highlights the general deficiency in Scottish and Irish diets of fresh, leafy vegetables, fruit and wholemeal bread. White bread has many vitamins removed in the milling process; only two have to be replaced by law and folic acid is not one of them. People in countries such as Sweden and Finland, although lacking fresh vegetables because of their climate, eat largely wholemeal bread, and the incidence of neural tube defects is one-tenth of that in the UK. It is not simply a lack of certain vitamins that causes malformation, rather perhaps, the interaction between toxic substances — nicotine, alcohol, drugs — and poor nutrition. Deficiency in vitamins, minerals and trace elements at the time of conception, or just before, may increase the sensitivity of a woman's body to any poisonous agent.

Women who are vulnerable, those on low incomes, can now be helped to prevent spina bifida and anencephaly by taking a standard multivitamin preparation both before and for at least two or three months after conception, when the foetuses are developing spinal cords and brain. Such treatment cuts down dramatically the number of babies with neural tube defects, to the normal level 1 in 200. For everyday advice to prevent malformations a good balanced diet should be eaten before conception and right through pregnancy.

Drugs

The thalidomide tragedy of the early 1960s drew attention to the potential danger of the taking of man-made drugs during pregnancy. It may be remembered that about two years or so after the introduction of thalidomide the incidence of certain limb malformations had risen sharply. Probably 7,000 babies were affected; some had no limbs, others had short or stunted arms and legs, besides internal abnormalities. Even aspirin or vitamin pills in *over-large* doses are under suspicion, the former as a possible cause of complicated deliveries, still birth and low birth weight.

On taking drugs during pregnancy Prof. R. S. Illingworth[28], Prof. of Child Health at Sheffield University said this: 'the best advice that one can offer to any pregnant woman is that she should take a medicine only when absolutely necessary — and that is rare'

German Measles

Infection of a pregnant mother by German measles virus is a well-known hazard to an unborn child who can be born blind or deaf or in severe cases have malformation of the brain and heart. When infection occurs during the first month of pregnancy there is an 80 per cent chance of the baby being deformed, a 60 per cent chance in the fourth month and a 10 per cent chance towards the end of pregnancy.[29] To prevent this it is sensible for young girls to be encouraged by their mothers to come into contact with infected friends before they reach child-bearing age, but vaccination against the disease is to be recommended for teenage girls and in 1977 in England and Wales, 70 per cent of girls have been vaccinated by their 14th birthday (see *Prevention and Health* 1977). Vaccination against German measles or use of other live vaccines should be avoided during pregnancy, because the live viruses in these vaccines can infect and damage the growing baby.

Low birth weight

It is worth repeating here that the most disturbing fact about child health between birth and the age of fifteen is the high number of baby and infant deaths; more than 70 per cent of deaths in England and Wales between birth and 15 occur in the first year of life.

The reasons for this enormous toll of life are numerous and complex. They include some of the avoidable environmental hazards to the unborn baby referred to earlier which are likely to hamper the growth of the foetus leading to babies of low birth weight. Low birth weight from whatever cause increases the risk of death during birth or in the first month of life. In 1974, 76 per cent of first-day deaths and 58 per cent of deaths within the first month of life occurred in low birth weight babies weighing 2.5 kg or less (see Court Report). To put high perinatal risks another way: in 1977 the perinatal mortality rate was 154.3 per 1000 low weight babies compared with 16.9 per 1000 for all births.

An important point to emphasise about the perinatal, neonatal (deaths in the first four weeks of life per 1,000 live births) and infant mortality rates is that all are higher on average in Social Classes IV (partly skilled) and V (unskilled). For perinatal mortality in Social Class I in England and Wales the rate is now 7.5 per 1,000 babies; in Social Class V it is 27.6; and among unsupported mothers it is 37.4. Nevertheless the average rate is now 14.6 (1979) per 1,000 and represents a heartening reduction in the past few years. In 1973 it was 21 per 1,000; and 50 years ago 62 per 1,000. Nevertheless we could do better: our rates are still 50 per cent above the best* (9.4 in Sweden for 1978) while there are marked regional variations in perinatal, neonatal and infant mortality. For perinatal mortality the West Midlands has almost 20 deaths per 1,000 babies, East Anglia has a rate of about 13, Wales 18.

The stark arithmetic of baby death in the perinatal and neonatal period each year in England and Wales is 9-10,000. About one third to one half of the deaths are preventable if modern knowledge and care were universally applied: that is 3,000-5,000 baby deaths need not happen. In addition the number of babies surviving each year with important handicaps that could have been prevented is of the order of 5,000. Thus the sum of death and permanent handicap in the perinatal (and neonatal) period is at least 8-10,000*.

It is likely that a good proportion of these baby deaths is due to smoking, to poor diet and to drinking alcohol in excess. In a broader sense they are the products of poverty, ignorance and psychological barriers that prevent women from using statutory services rather than a lack of concern for their child's welfare. In the long term raising the standard of living and of the knowledge of the part parents can play in the birth of a normally formed and healthy baby are the best remedies for preventing baby deaths.

Barriers to the use of antenatal clinics by mothers are well known: overcrowding, distance, big families, a mechanistic atmosphere in some clinics with lack of proper opportunities for a mother to discuss her feelings and anxieties. Evidence from the recent report on *Perinatal and Neonatal Mortality** stresses the need to improve the "cattle market" conditions in some clinics and to reduce the number of visits by low-risk mothers but to persuade "high-risk" mothers to use them. These high-risk women include older mothers, those from the lower socio-economic classes and those from certain ethnic groups particularly Asian and West Indian where a high rate of baby and infant death prevails.

Perinatal and Neonatal Mortality (1980) HMSO.

Teachers together with increased support in the ante-natal and infant stages from Health Visitors, can play a positive role in teaching parents and future parents what to do and not to do in pregnancy, that many baby deaths and handicaps are preventable and that it is crucial to attend as early as possible in pregnancy for ante-natal care. Surveys show that perinatal mortality is five times the overall national figure when there are no pre-natal visits and four times when there is only one. This is what Neville Butler[30] wrote nearly ten years ago but it is still true:

> It has proved possible to trace some origins of this social disadvantage right back to early pregnancy. Thus, a high proportion of less fortunate foetuses lying within the wombs of mothers in Social Class 4 and 5 failed to meet their obstetrician in the early weeks of pregnancy. Fewer mothers in the lower socio-economic groups had medical attendance in labour. A greater proportion of the manual-class mothers smoked in pregnancy, now known to be a major factor in increasing the proportion of low birthweight babies.

It might be added here that Dr. Arthur Wynn's* recipe for increasing the chances of serious malformations sums up much of what has been said in this chapter:

> The woman who eats junk food, slims before and during pregnancy, smokes, takes aspirin, tranquillisers, or any other drug, lives by a main road with its fumes and lead dust and enjoys her gin and tonic.

Once the baby is born the importance of good nutrition can be explained, including the need to breast-feed when possible since human milk not only contains the right mixture of foods at the right temperature and in the quantity the baby needs but contains cells which protect the baby from gastroenteritis during the first vulnerable months of life. Breast feeding may also protect from cot death because breast milk contains more biotin, one of the B group of vitamins, than bottle milk. Biotin deficiency may leave a baby in a vulnerable condition in which death could be triggered by a stress, such as a missed meal or excessive heat or cold, that would not normally affect it.

All mothers should be encouraged to breast-feed their babies for the minimum of two weeks and preferably for the first four to six

*Sunday Times, 13th April, 1980

months of life. Not all mothers can or wish to breast-feed and modified dried baby milks are available. Suckling also helps the mother to slim after pregnancy, to develop the close bonding between a mother and child which is so important in the early stages of life, to reduce the risk of getting a breast tumour in later life and to control the urge to batter a baby when irritated by it. Mothers in Social Classes IV and V breast-feed their babies less often than those in Social Classes I and II.

Other important matters to be taught are cleanliness in storing food, the need to use sterile bottles and to keep a baby warm.

The robust guidance given by the Wakefield and District Sanitary Aid Society (1900) on 'how to rear a healthy baby' (see endnote 9) is informative of the times and besides being interesting contains some sound advice, then as now. It should be noted that recent research confirms that human milk is best for infants and that bottle feeding especially with unmodified cow's milk foods, can present hazards to some infants (see *Prevention and Health* 1977):

> FOOD — if the mother's milk is good and plentiful, the child should have no other food whatever until seven months old. If the mother has not enough milk, cow's milk should be given in addition to it, but not in place of it: the two milks will not disagree. While suckling the mother should take plain and wholesome food: stimulants are not necessary, and spirits are distinctly harmful . . .
>
> Never give the baby tea or coffee. Children would be much sturdier if given warm milk instead of tea or coffee until four years old.
>
> The following things are also harmful for little children, beer, spirits, wine, new bread, currants, unripe fruit, soothing syrups, or teething powders. The use of the two last undermine the health of many children. No medicine should be given except by doctor's advice.
>
> A baby's clothing should be clean and warm, but not tight about the body . . .

Despite advice of all kinds from 'experts' it is also necessary to encourage parents and future parents to trust their own common sense and instincts about child care. Much of what is written later in this book about the mother-child bond, about language development, about play is what most ordinary, warm-hearted people know in their bones. But the more insights scientific evidence can provide, the better parents and others are equipped to assess the reliability of what is presented as common sense, while the more instinctive motives are reinforced.

Chapter 4

Development of Embryo and Foetus

The most critical stage in the development of a baby, the formation of the spinal cord and brain, is complete by the end of the embryonic period of eight weeks from fertilization while the special sense organs, the eyes and ears, are also *structurally* well advanced. Indeed the major structures and systems are established during the foetal stage. Even though the brain and head develop very fast early on in life, the brain is not functional. The most important functional development occurs after birth through learning and the brain is poised for learning within hours of birth. The sex of the child is also obvious by the end of the seventh week (see *Before Birth*).

At the beginning of the foetal period — the ninth week after fertilization — the foetus is about three cm long. The foetal stage lasts for 30 weeks until birth. During this stage the various parts of the body differentiate and mature sufficiently to enable survival outside the uterus. It is a period marked by fast growth. The fastest growth in length takes place at about four months from conception when growth is going on at a rate of 10 to 12 cm each month. Before this, growth is slow and later on it declines and the foetus may even lose weight if pregnancy is unduly prolonged. It is probably at this time, when the food supply has fallen below its optimal level, that a foetus becomes unduly susceptible to birth damage.

Overall from the ninth week until birth the length increases from three cm to about 50 cm and the weight from four g to over 3000g. Up to about six months after conception most of the increase in foetal weight is due to protein accumulation as the body cells are built up. From then on fat accumulates to give an energy reserve available after birth. The diversion of this energy to the foetus marks a considerable drain on the mother in the last weeks of pregnancy.[31]

Certain essential activities take place and are established before birth in preparation for the needs that arise after birth: the swallowing and sucking reflexes are perfected and sets of muscles to assist breathing are active and the formation of urine begins.

Towards the very end of pregnancy from about 36 weeks from conception to birth at around 40 weeks, the baby slows down in rate of growth and this may be the effect of space in the uterus.

Twins slow down sooner, when their combined weight is equal to that of a 36 week old single baby.

If the child's hereditary blueprint is for largeness, the slowing-down mechanism helps such a child to be born easily to a small woman. The particularly big child has an inheritance which is timed to make itself felt only after birth and thus given the right conditions for growth in the uterus, a baby born small grows fast in the first few years and again in adolescence under the guidance of heredity.

This book is largely concerned with child development and learning patterns and for this reason brain development will be singled out for more detailed treatment now but in passing it may be noted that about three weeks after conception, the heart beats, at seven weeks sex is distinguishable externally, at 12 weeks the forelimbs are well developed, at 18 weeks the hindlimbs reach final proportions, at 24 weeks the body is lean but well proportioned and about then its lungs can be inflated. (Reports of babies supposed to have been aborted at well under 24 weeks and then heard crying, must be mistaken since a child cannot cry unless its lungs can inflate).

Early brain growth

The big spurt in brain growth starts towards the end of the first six months of pregnancy and slows down at around two years. There is however a *minor* growth spurt earlier on which lasts from the twelfth to the eighteenth week of pregnancy. This minor spurt simply represents the multiplication of nerve cells. The *major* growth spurt reflects growth and branching of the nerve cells with no increase in their number and marks a sensitive time for brain development.

A generalization may be applied to all animals including man, that nerve cells are most sensitive to the effects of the environment during periods of rapid growth. Thus environmental influences referred to earlier, such as smoking, drugs, alcohol and perhaps other toxic substances found in water, food and the atmosphere may affect the unborn child. Once the child is born the fast growing brain is equally

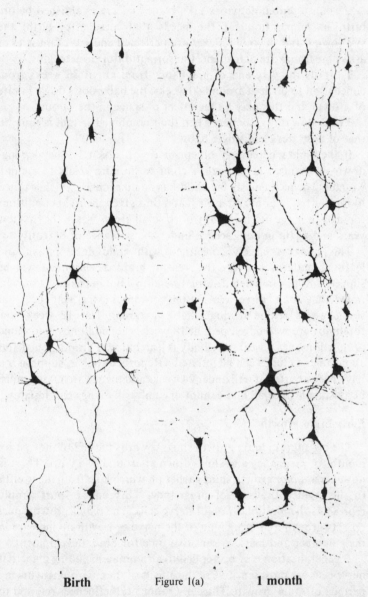

Birth   Figure 1(a)   **1 month**

Neurones (nerve cells) in the cerebral cortex of a child at birth, of another at the age of one month, and another at the age of four years. Each nerve cell shown is a pyramidal cell. It has a triangular body with basal dendrites running in all directions and the main apical dendrite stretching out towards the surface of the cortex where it gives off many

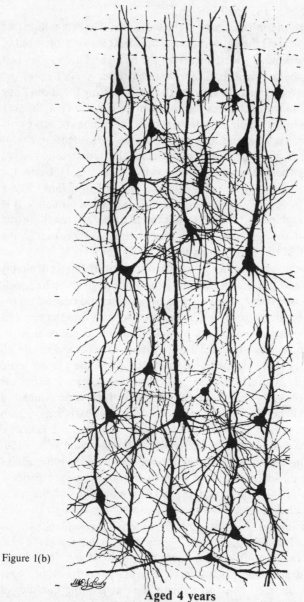

Figure 1(b)

Aged 4 years

branches. It is thought, but not proved, that the richness of branching and connecting of the dendrites is important in the development of the brain's capabilities. From CONEL, J. Le Roy (1939). *Post natal development of the human cerebral cortex.* Harvard. (The date 1939 refers to the publication date of volume 1 in the series.)

impressionable to the environment.

Not all parts of the brain grow at the same rate. The cerebellum (see fig. 2 on pages 56-7) the coordinator of muscular movement, is out of step in its development with the rest of the brain and grows very fast from shortly before birth until about a year after.[32]

During the major growth spurt of the brain, lasting for about 27 or 28 months, important changes take place in the brain cortex, the grey matter of the brain which helps us to think. The billions of nerve cells in the cortex are growing and branching to form dense webs of connections. The parts of the nerve cells that connect (at nerve synapses) are the fine tendrils called dendrites (see Fig. 1). Under the microscope a slice of grey matter from a child of four looks like a dense forest of branches. At birth there are only a few branches. It is thought, though not established, that the richness of branching and connecting of the dendrites in the grey matter is important in the development of the brain's capabilities.

The sprouting and proliferation of dendritic branching is probably under the broad guidance of heredity but there is likely to be a wide margin of possibilities for development which could depend on the quality of experience provided by parents, schools and the rest of a child's environment. Educators have been quick to notice that the brain of animals provided with a wide variety of tasks and of stimuli develop many more dendritic connections than one placed in an impoverished environment. If the idea is accepted that the enviroment of the baby and young child can influence the number of dendritic branches, it would not be surprising that early experiences might produce important and lasting effects on behaviour. Likewise the growth of new connections between nerve cells could account for certain lasting memories, whether formed in a child's or an adult's brain.[33] The difficulty is to find ways of testing these speculations.

In man it is very likely that the nerve connections of the brain continue to change and develop throughout life. Though this last statement cannot yet be proved, direct biochemical evidence shows that the brain is in a dynamic state, for the protein that it is made of is continually being built up and broken down and may reflect the growth and destruction of dendrites. Perhaps this continual turnover of the brain material helps to explain the outstanding qualities of plasticity and resilience which are hall marks of the human mind.

It will be clear now that the brain grows very fast in the foetus. At about 8 weeks from conception it weighs about 2.5g; at birth about

380g, about 11 per cent of body weight. It continues to grow fast after birth; at age five it is, in boys, about 1250 g and in girls, 1220 g. By about age 10 the brain is almost (95 per cent) full grown in both, around 1400 g for boys, 1300 for girls.

The major growth spurt of the brain may be a time of a 'once only' opportunity to grow properly and as suggested earlier deprivation whether in food or stimulus may be harmful.

The protein requirements of the growing brain are likely to be great. Just before birth and in the first year of life a baby's brain is growing at the rate of one or two mg every minute (Brierley, J.K. op.cit.) and needs large quantities of protein from a good diet of milk, meat and eggs by the mother and, after birth as referred to earlier, from mother's milk supplemented by other foods after about three months. Galen in AD 100 had this to say about feeding: 'She shall feed the child only on milk until he has cut his front teeth, then it is well to accustom him to more solid food, as women do of their own accord having learned this by experience'. This advice is as sound now as it was then.

The *quantity* of brain matter has perhaps been over-stressed but less than 1000g is incompatible with normality. What is more important than weight in the growth and development of the brain is its internal organization and in particular, dendritic branching. In a nutshell it is not quantity which is important but connectivity.

Sexing the brain

The sex of a child is laid down in the brain (Brierley, J.K. op.cit.) early on through the action of the XY trigger, referred to earlier. At first the embryo is neuter but by the end of seven weeks the sex organs are recognizable, male if an XY genetic constitution, female if XX. Once the foetal testes are formed, at about the twelfth week after conception, they produce the male sex hormone which acts as a chemical (hormonal) signal to sex the hypothalamus by altering the growth and pattern of certain nerve cells in it. The hypothalamus is the part of the brain whose job is to regulate the glands and parts of the nervous system. In the absence of the Y and consequently the absence of male hormone, the brain of the foetus develops according to the female pattern. Eve, so the Old Testament says, was made from a rib of Adam, but the evidence is that maleness is carved by the Y out of a basically female pattern.

The second 'phase' of sex development does not take place until adolescence, which will be returned to in Chapter 13. Briefly, through a chemical signal from the pituitary gland, which takes its cues from the hypothalamus, the monthly waxing and waning tides of hormones commence in the female; in the male the non-rhythmic pattern. What causes the hypothalamus to initiate these events is not known.

Besides the hormonal sexing of the hypothalmus there are other sex differences in brain development; again these will be described and discussed in relation to learning in Chapter 7.

At birth, then, all the brain cells have been formed and the sex of the child has been established. As every mother knows, the limbs and body of the foetus can move and perhaps already hearing is activated by the sound of the mother's heart, intestines and muscles. As indicated earlier in Chapter 1 the new born baby's brain is open and flexible and ready to experience basic sensations from the moment he or she is born.

Chapter 5

Screening before Birth

To give birth to an abnormal baby is a shattering experience for parents. Equally, a fear that a defect of some kind might run in the family can cause untold worry. On the basis of present knowledge there are unfortunately no grounds as yet for optimism about the possibility of preventing *conception* of most congenital abnormalities — mental subnormality and malformations. Positive ways of preventing such a child being born are at present only the prevention of conception altogether or the elimination of the foetus by abortion; and both these methods are controversial and rightly a matter for the individual or the couple.

Genetic counselling

Modern genetical studies have identified many hereditary conditions and diseases such as haemophilia, and the list is growing. Though most of these cannot be detected before birth, advice on the chances of having an affected child can be given. Couples seeking advice on the chances of having an abnormal baby are always told of a probability, never a certainty, by genetic counsellors at major hospitals: 'Your baby has a one in four chance of being affected' might be the sort of advice given if two people each possessed an inherited trait. It is important to remember that these odds are given in terms of averages. In one single family of four children several may be affected or none. The one in four chance is only meaningful when many families are considered and the results averaged out. One important point is that the stated odds for a trait cropping up are the same for each successive child in a family, regardless of what happened to the others.

A person may be a 'carrier' of the trait for a certain abnormality but not have the disease himself. Technically the trait is called 'recessive' because it does not show itself. Each one of us carries, on average, three of these hidden recessive traits. But if a carrier marries another carrier (a rare event, as we shall see) there is a probability that one out of four of the children will be affected as referred to above.

To give an example, about one person in 72 in Britain carries an inherited trait for albinism but only about one baby in every 20,000 is an albino (see *Biology and the Social Crisis*). This makes it clear that although the frequency of carriers of the 'bad' recessive gene is high, the *chance* of producing an affected child is low, because of the rarity of carriers marrying. In fact, approximately 80 albinos are born in Britain each year. The point is that the trait has to be present in double dose for it to cause the disease in the child; a single dose does not have any obvious effect but that child will be a carrier himself.

Three screening techniques

If the mother is already pregnant, techniques are now available to let the parents know (if they wish to) whether the unborn child is afflicted with a handicap like Down's syndrome or spina bifida but to cope with the emotional effects of testing is hard if a mother has decided to find out.

Three techniques are producing dramatic successes. One of these is amniocentesis which involves the withdrawal of 15-21 ml of fluid from the membranes surrounding the baby. The technique is based on the fact that the foetus sheds cells into the fluid surrounding it; the cells are cultured and their chromosomes examined for abnormalities. Other tests following amniocentesis can help to diagnose over 60 rare metabolic disorders. Most tests are carried out in the sixteenth week of pregnancy because by then enough fluid surrounds the foetus for a sample to be taken safely. In Britain, the 1967 Abortion Act allowed mothers, who were at risk of having a seriously handicapped child, the opportunity to have the pregnancy terminated. If amniocentesis is carried out at the sixteenth week and the suspected abnormality is due to a chromosome mistake (e.g. Down's syndrome) it takes about a fortnight to check the results. After 28 weeks the law does not allow a pregnancy to be terminated. There is however, a 2 per cent risk of miscarriage associated with amniocentesis which precludes screening of all pregnant women and is only justified in mothers of high risk because of their age (40+), or a history of a previously affected child.

It is however now possible to tell with a fair degree of accuracy at 16-18 weeks of pregnancy — the optimum time for tests — whether a baby has defects such as spina bifida or anencephaly, by the amount of a protein, alpha-foeto protein, present in the blood. When the level is substantially higher than normal it is practically certain that the foetus is abnormal and the mother can be offered termination. The AFP blood test is preferable as a first screening test since there is no risk of abortion as with amniocentesis (see *Prevention and Health*). It is usual to check a positive diagnosis of abnormality by the AFP test by a third technique — ultra sound scanning — before finally offering an abortion. Ultra-sound scanning uses the principle of echo-location to map the shape and position of the foetus whose pattern is displayed as an image on a TV screen. This remarkable development can detect anencephaly, hydrocephaly and the more severe cases of spina bifida as well as gestational age and multiple pregnancies.

The three techniques described are indeed remarkable advances but it should be remembered that they will be out of date in ten years time, to be replaced by even more sophisticated ones. No matter what advice is given during genetic counselling or after the screening tests described, it is only advice. Usually it is informed and constructive but rightly the decision whether to risk having children, or for a mother to have an abortion in the case of a suspected abnormal pregnancy, is left to the good sense and judgment of the future parents.

Laws about abortion, as about anything else concerning morals or personal decisions, are blunt instruments. They influence human nature little: 'How small of all that human hearts endure, that part, which laws or kings can cause or cure', wrote Dr. Johnson.

Freedom of choice on personal matters is absolutely right but it needs full knowledge of facts, alternatives and consequences. Termination of a healthy pregnancy is one such choice about which a base of fact is necessary (see also Chapter 16).

Chapter 6

Patterns of growth in the early years of childhood

Eighty to a hundred years ago infant mortality was very great; parents then had large families but did not expect all their children to live. New-born babies and infants have always been frail and vulnerable but in the relatively short space of time since the reader's father or grandfather was born, childbirth has become much safer. Now birth and the first years of life are less hazardous than they were, at least in developed parts of the world. There are fewer children in families and greater expectations for their health and education. This optimism has solid foundations. Besides safer birth, improvements in housing, cleanliness, nutrition and immunization have almost wiped out diseases that killed babies and young children in their thousands. All the same there are, as indicated earlier, many remaining black spots in the health and life chances of many children as recorded in infant and perinatal mortality rates.

The concern of this book with physical health and baby care is marginal to its main theme of child development looked at from an educational point of view, but good health and sound development of body and mind are closely intertwined. It may be added here that much to do with child rearing is a matter of trusting instincts. In this context the writings of Galen about AD 100 have been quoted already as an example of wisdom, clear observation and commonsense. Here is Galen once more on the condition of the fretful child:

> I have also noted that his cot and his wrappings were too dirty and the infant himself dirty and unwashed and I have ordered

him to be bathed and that he should have clean napkins and when these things were done the infant has stopped kicking and settled off in a long sleep.

Settling a fretful child such as this, feeding, cuddling, and making 'silly' faces and noises and, when older, providing a secure framework of order for him to grow up in, are all part of early rearing in which commonsense and 'instinct' give the sure touch. It is surprising and comforting that the findings of ethologists, physicians, neurologists and psychiatrists have tended to confirm much of what most mothers and teachers of young children know in their bones already.

Early growth patterns

Patterns of growth in children are complicated and fairly well-defined. No prediction can be made at birth about a child's ultimate height because the size of a new born baby reflects the environment in the mother's uterus and not its future pattern of growth. A boy may be born small but grow large because of his genetic endowment. Not all genes are active at birth and some begin to act only after a period of time. Perhaps this phased effect of genes lends support to the common observation that children grow to resemble their parents increasingly as they grow older.

The average boy at four is 58 per cent and at five 62 per cent of his adult height, so comparisons can be made. An average girl, always more advanced in her growing than a boy, is already 62 per cent of her adult height at four; 66 per cent at five. The 'girls-first' rule is shown by the fact that she reaches 50 per cent of her adult height at 1.75 years compared with two years in a boy. There is so much variation among normal children however that this information cannot be used to work out how tall a child will become when he or she is grown up.

After birth a child grows faster than at any other time in life (but not as fast as before birth) usually doubling its birth weight in the first six months and reaching about three times its birth weight by a year. Even so from birth onwards the speed of growth declines compared with before birth. Just as a car may speed up or slow down within an hour or so the speed of growth may change from one part of a year to another, but this is not to say that growth takes place in fits and starts — it is a smooth process.

Up to about the age of four or five the speed of growth falls dramatically and from then up to the start of the adolescent spurt, at about 11 on average in girls and 13 in boys (the maximum speed is on average 12 in girls and 14 in boys) come the years of unspectacular growth when the rate remains practically constant with a height gain of about one cm per year. During the period of rapid growth in infancy a sufficient supply of Vitamin D is important for the calcification of bone, and the supplement of this vitamin may be necessary in the winter months up to the age of five and in children where there is a risk of malnutrition with either inadequate or imbalanced diets. Care is necessary, however, as overdose of Vitamin D can be dangerous.

Boys and girls

The growth curves of boys and girls from birth to about five differ slightly. At birth the average boy is growing a bit faster than a girl but the velocity equalizes at about seven months. After this the boys' rate of growth falls off more than the girls until aged four, and from then on there is no difference until adolescence.

A fat layer begins to be laid down 10 to 14 weeks before birth (26-30 weeks after conception) and infants born at the normal time have about 12 per cent of body weight as fat. Fat increases greatly in the first year of life. Girls are already a bit plumper than boys at birth, a trait that becomes more marked during childhood. But from about a year to around seven, both slim down and become sturdier; muscle replaces fat as infants turn their attention from eating and growing to walking and playing. In the arm, for example, the circumference remains the same from four to seven but the muscle/fat ratio changes in favour of muscle. In other words the pre-school and infant years are those in which the chunky physique of the newborn changes into the more elongated build of the child.

A number of sex differences in growth patterns quite apart from the reproductive organs, are present before puberty. Boys have longer and thicker forearms, relative to upper arms and as we shall see in a later chapter a boy's legs grow faster than the trunk just before puberty to give him relatively longer legs than a girl. This latter feature is mainly due to the longer period of pre-adolescent growth in boys.

Children of five or six are well aware of sex differences: 'boys are rougher, they fight'; 'men don't have babies — boys have different bodies'; but 'you get tom-boys and tom-girls'; 'they (boys) don't speak the same, some girls talk quietly, boys' voices are rougher and deeper'.

The description of growth in height given a moment ago is a coarse one and there are finer periods of growth which underlie the general growth rate. Within a year's space, as parents must have noticed, children of between five and nine do not grow at the same speed. For some the slowest growth takes place during Autumn and Winter, the fastest between January and July. For others there are comparable changes in growth rate but apparently independent of season. Before about five, when the speed of growth is decelerating rapidly, and during the adolescent spurt, seasonal changes in growth rate are masked by the speed of the overall change. Growth in weight is usually fastest in the Autumn.

There is some slight evidence that day length, which varies during the seasons, may affect growth perhaps by influencing the glands controlling growth, through the eyes. In totally blind children the rate of growth does not vary as much with the seasons as it does with children of normal sight. This is not to say that blind children grow at a constant rate but their fastest and slowest growth may take place in any season.[34] This fact however applies to many children with normal sight.

Early growth of the brain and head

Change in height is normally taken as an overall measure of growth but in man this masks a remarkable pattern of differential growth, particularly marked in the early years of life. Up to puberty the brain and head, including the sense organs, are growing faster than the body and it is only during and after the adolescent growth spurt at about 18 or 20, that the body catches up. Thus at the age of five the brain and head are about 80 per cent grown, the body only about 40 per cent. At around seven, the brain and head are 90 per cent grown, the body not quite at the half way mark.

Like all products of evolution this pattern of growth is a highly efficient one for learning because up to puberty children are adapted for passing through a long period when they are relatively small, weak and dependent — in a physical sense. Yet the brain and sense organs are well developed and rapidly absorb and use experience from the environment. During the early years of life, in fact right up to puberty, a child is under 'tuition'; he can be kept in order and taught and can play with others without them hurting each other much. Because in the long past the human life span was short, evolution time-tabled these dozen or so years from birth to puberty as critical ones for learning. The growth spurt of puberty changes children into adults, themselves capable (in evolutionary terms) of dominating the young and caring for them.

Evolution has seen to it, therefore, that the brain at birth is poised ready to learn and to go on learning fast during the long childhood up to puberty. The brain itself is finely tuned and is in a two-way dynamic relationship with the environment and seems to strengthen its powers by practice. During these early years a child needs plenty of stimulus, play and language experience and good models to imitate if he is to develop well. If a child is socially and culturally deprived or underestimated at school by his teachers he is likely to make poor progress. The development of his mind could be hampered, not necessarily by physical damage to the brain by altering nerve pathways — though this is quite possible — but by creating an unsatisfactory state of mind by poor motivation and by learning to have a poor expectation of life. In this context *Primary Education in England* indicated that children in inner city schools were more likely than others to be underestimated by their teachers and least likely to be given work which extended their capabilities. The evidence suggested that further improvement in the children's performance was possible.

Some factors affecting growth

Apart from some abnormalities, growth rates at any stage of development can be hampered by bad feeding, disease and unhappiness. When health and well-being improve a return to normal height is achieved by a big catch-up growth to a normal pattern. How this catch-up growth is regulated is not understood but its machinery is so sensitive and effective that it allows growth to return almost completely to its previous pattern after a set-back (see *The Growing Brain*). This is a sensible arrangement for in bad times the child stops growing, saves his energy and waits for better times.

Happiness, as we all know, is essential to good health and growth in children but it is hard to pin down exactly how it operates. Commonsense tells us that good food, warmth, comfort, cleanliness, love and a ready ear to worries are all important to health and growth and 'good' homes are not necessarily dependent upon plenty of money or property. There is one classical case which 'proves' that good growth is linked with love and happiness. It happened in Germany just after the last war. Extra food was given to children but it did not result in the expected growth. This was because it was given by a disagreeable, harsh and repressive sister-in-charge who frightened the children. She had favourites, however, who benefitted from the extra food by gain in weight (see Tanner, J.M., op.cit). There is some evidence too that some children do not grow so well in term-time as in school holidays no matter whether they are day pupils or at boarding school.

The effect of stress on happiness, appetite and consequently nutrition and growth is clearly complex, certainly involves the body glands, and needs further investigation. The Bible sums up human wisdom on the matter: 'Better a dinner of herbs where love is than a stalled ox and hatred therewith'. This is the simple message that needs to be taken seriously and acted upon.

What has been written about growth in general terms should not conceal the important fact that each child will have its own pattern of growth. Some children are fast, some slow growers, something that will be considered further in the chapter on adolescence. To treat all as equal is to follow a programme which is suitable for the few who happen to fit the mean course of growth.

Chapter 7
The Brain

Some of the functions of man's brain mark him off from all other animal species — they enable us to speak, to cooperate with each other, to think and to laugh. Marvellously, the majority of children have the capacity to understand and speak a language, to think symbolically, to classify sensory events and words into categories, to infer relationships between things, to deduce implications, to analyse the environment into coherent elements, to relate past experience to present information (memory) and to spot logical flaws in an argument. The brain is also responsible for our doubts, fears, joys, longings, imagination and moral sense; all qualities that lift us above other animals. Unfortunately about 5 per cent of children have some brain damage which denies them the capacity to enjoy one or more of these qualities.

All of these commonplace activities and feelings are determined by 'lower' and 'higher' centres in the brain. These include the star of the higher centres, the cerebral cortex, the human thinking cap, an enormous sheet of thousands of millions of nerve cells which we use when we think.

It would be a great help to education if we knew more about how the brain of each individual child develops and works, but two major obstacles prevent any clear understanding. One is the sparsity of facts about the physical basis of higher mental function. The other is the almost hopeless tangle of related environmental factors which, with heredity, shape personality and intellect. Some Darwin of the mind will, it is to be hoped, fit the pieces of research together to give us a theory of learning based on science which education presently lacks. It will help us to understand how we read, how we teach children to read with greater understanding, how we see ourselves, shapes, faces and people. We have a glimmering already of how we do some of these things.

Brain surgeons, when looking at a living brain, say that its strangest quality is its stillness. Its shape and appearance give no clue to its function and the ancients concluded that it was an organ for cooling the blood. The fact that nerves run to it from all over the body and away from it shows, however, that the brain has overall control. It is not a single structure but consists basically of four parts (the cortex, inner core, cerebellum and bulb), all closely enmeshed by nerves. (see Fig. 2)

Grey matter

On the outside is the grey matter of the cortex, tightly folded to give an enormous surface area to the brain. In fact more than half the area of the cortex lies tucked into the folds. The cortex is really a double structure split down the middle, but the halves (the left and right hemispheres) are joined by rich nerve connections allowing the parts of the brain to interact in complex ways. One hemisphere of the cortex, the left, is detailed to handle the problem of speech but of course, speech is more than one thing. Spoken (motor) speech is located in a small well-defined area, but other speech areas — for writing and for understanding spoken and written speech — are not so clearly defined and may vary in position from brain to brain. Indeed it should be stressed that although functions are broadly localized, the brain has a level of organizational plasticity that allows alternative channels to develop, so that destruction of one does not necessarily abolish the functions. Chapter 8 considers the resilience of the brain in more detail but it is known for example that the plasticity of the brain can allow the programming of a satisfactory, even exemplary, intellectual function into a relatively small volume of grey matter (*World Medicine* 3 May 1980). In brain terms, what you never had, you may never miss because the brain adapts and uses alternative strategies in its wiring patterns and learning processes. One brief example may be useful: a hydrocephalic man's brain-scan picture revealed no visual cortex yet his visual perception was well above average. Care needs to be taken however, in the interpretation of these remarkable findings with hydrocephalics. The same quantity of cortex may be present as in a normal brain, but spread out more thinly. What is necessary is for a brain-cell count to be made. Nevertheless, it does seem as if a considerable amount of spare brain

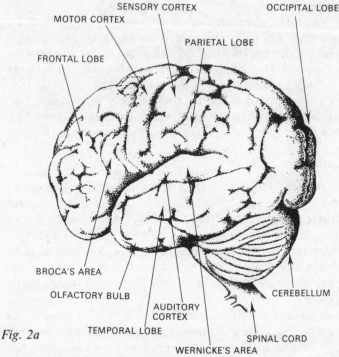

LEFT HEMISPHERE (outside)

Fig. 2a

Cerebral Cortex Grey matter covering surface of cerebral hemispheres, 3-4 millimetres thick.

Motor Cortex A strip of cortex which controls specific muscle acts organized by the whole cortex.

Sensory Cortex A strip of cortex which receives 'sensations' from the skin.

Auditory Cortex Area of cortex in temporal lobe. Receives reports of auditory sensation.

Olfactory Lobe. The smell brain. In man, visual clues are more important than smell but particular smells may suddenly arouse complicated visual and other memories. The olfactory sense has strong emotional value.

Occipital Lobe The posterior lobe of a cerebral hemisphere; concerned with vision.

Visual Cortex Area of cortex at the rear of each hemisphere in the occipital lobes which receives reports of visual sensation via the thalamus.

Parietal Lobe The side area of a cerebral hemisphere. Seems to control relationship between body and mind. Injuries can disturb knowledge of where parts of the body are.

Frontal Lobe. The anterior portion of a cerebral hemisphere. Probably concerned with inhibition, especially repressing inappropriate behaviour.

Temporal Lobe A part of the side of a cerebral hemisphere underlying the temple. Largely concerned with sound and its interpretation. Together with the hippocampi plays a crucial role in memory.

Broca's Area Found in one hemisphere only usually the left. Controls motor speech. Damage causes any speech that remains to be curt, telegraphic and laborious.

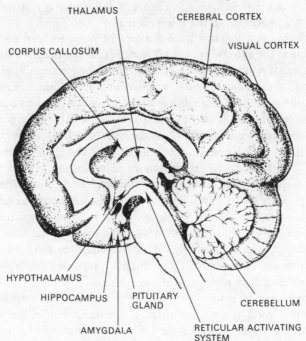

RIGHT HEMISPHERE (inside)

THALAMUS

CEREBRAL CORTEX

CORPUS CALLOSUM

VISUAL CORTEX

HYPOTHALAMUS

HIPPOCAMPUS

PITUITARY GLAND

CEREBELLUM

AMYGDALA

RETICULAR ACTIVATING SYSTEM

Fig. 2b

Wernicke's Area Found in one hemisphere only, usually the left. May be involved in the understanding and analysis of speech.

Corpus Callosum An enormous strip of millions of nerves which link the two halves of the brain.

Thalamus A relay station at the centre of the brain which sends signals from various sensory systems to the cortex. Said to give emotional tone to cortical experience.

Hypothalamus. Small area in the basal part of the brain. The supreme regulator of instinctive behaviour (thirst, aggression, sex). Works through pituitary and nervous system.

Pituitary Gland. Attached to the under surface of the brain and largely controlled by hypothalamus. In turn controls other glands and body function.

Hippocampus Tucked inside the temporal lobes. Enables learning to take place perhaps by laying down or retrieving long-term memories.

Amygdala A basal part of the brain which regulates aggressive and other emotional behaviour.

Reticular activating system. Large untidy tangle of nerves near the centre of the brain possibly important in the arousal to action and in sleep.

Cerebellum. Large lobe at the back of the brain which organizes complex muscle teamwork for actions merely sketched out by the conscious mind. Has close relationship with the cerebral cortex.

Spinal Cord The slender part of the central nervous system extending from the brain down the back. The backbone surrounds and protects the cord.

tissue exists which allows a wide safety margin against damage. So just as an individual can live on a quarter of a kidney, so he might live with a reduction in the brain cortex.

It may be asked how the brain uses the messages from a sense organ such as the eye. When a child works at his painting, messages of an electrical nature are sent from the retina along nerve cells to the visual part of the cortex which is activated to give him a picture of his painting in three-dimensional array, brightness and colour. What is sent to the brain is not of course an accurate copy of the picture but a simplified electrical and chemical code which is interpreted by the brain as the painting — inside his head — though it appears in front of him. To state the problem more generally: visual perception is an interpretation of information reaching the retina which needs experience to interpret. It is not known how the cortex classifies and combines stimuli into shape and colour though experiments with animals show that there are cells in the brain cortex which respond electrically to a whole range of shapes: slits, lines and even cells tuned to paw and face shapes. It is very unlikely that the human brain would have detectors which would recognize a specific face because this would lead to penny-in-the-slot responses. Rather more likely (and there is good evidence for them) is the presence of cells in the cortex which react to broad classes of stimuli: amount of contour, size, movement, brightness, nearness and so on. These cells must process information at different levels, some cells receiving and decoding a convergence of sensory input. This sort of flexibility of function in the fine structure of brain cells would enable the brain to make sense of a complex, changing environment and also to adapt to new circumstances. These generalized abilities of feature-detecting cells in the human brain, rather than highly specific ones, lend weight to the basic notion of a child's open, flexible mind.

The brain is not haphazard in scanning the environment: rather it seems to search for meaningful combinations of features which give clues to their nature and function. Thus, when certain contours are presented they are put together in ways that allow us, for instance, to sit down on a horizontal and four vertical lines that we call a stool. Margaret Donaldson[35] in *Children's Minds* quotes some experiments in which four-year-olds were asked to decide whether statements were true or false in relation to pictures and then recorded eye movements as the children searched the pictures for clues and reached a decision. Four-year olds could organize their search patterns but irrelevant pictures could throw a child off track. Similarly with children of four or five, art work will follow a lawful pattern. The units or parts of a drawing are related to one another in a sequence and the sequences change with age: children usually move from top to bottom and left to right. A man is usually drawn by a pre-school child as a circle with some face details, then legs. Some stop there leaving armless figures. Others as Jacqueline Goodnow[36] states, 'go back to finish', to add arms, ears, hair and so on. This suggests that the brain has become 'adept' at monitoring, at running an eye over a piece of work to see if all the pieces are present; this again reinforces the notion that the brain is searching for a pattern. Thus the plan of action that the brain has at this age is a limited one but nevertheless a dawning power: to manipulate facts, to play with them and arrange them into patterns.

To add weight to this hypothesis J.Z. Young, (see *Programs of the Brain*) suggests that the brain is likely to have a strategy for examining the features of our world in order to find first points, then lines, regions, surfaces, bodies and eventually objects that have meaning or use; in other words to stick to a hypothesis which is being tested before a decision is reached and not to be diverted by irrelevancies.

Memory

Returning to broad areas of the cortex and their function, the temporal lobe lying on each hemisphere like the thumb of a boxing glove beside the fist, seems to play an essential part in the retrieval of memories. Tucked into each temporal lobe is a twisted structure, like a sea horse, the hippocampus. Perhaps the temporal cortex acts like a complicated filing cabinet and the hippocampus is the key which unlocks it and makes available a strip of memory.[37] In normal life the pair of hippocampus/temporal lobes might act to scan and match new information coming to the brain from the senses against a record of past experience retrieved from a vast filing cabinet of memories stored in the cortex. Though it is speculation, perhaps new information is held in a temporary memory while comparisons are made and integrated between what is happening now and items of past experience flashed back for inspection. The integration of present and past is called 'active memory' and what the brain tells us to do as a result of these comparisons depends on the base-line of information in the memory store and its quality.

It is important to emphasize the somewhat speculative nature of what has just been said about the mechanism of memory. The temporal lobes and hippocampi have been mentioned but it is risky to take a strong view on localization. Memories, in keeping with the complex neurone web, seem to be stored rather diffusely within the brain tissue and are at present elusive. Memory can certainly be damaged by removing parts of the brain but large areas have to be removed to damage memory severely and even when this is done long-term memory still survives.

The importance of the memory systems in a child's learning is dealt with later: sufficient to say now that memory develops strongly between three and nine months.

Interestingly the amount of quiet sleep in a baby, constant from around three to nine months shows an increase at about nine months which is the age when memory improves. Though this is in the realms of speculation again, it does seem that in the young, when new nerve connections are being formed and the wiring patterns of the brain are changing, sleep is of particular importance.

It is thought that large areas of the brain cortex are 'uncommitted' (see Penfield op.cit.) at birth. In other words a baby is born with a brain most of which is like a blank slate ready to be filled with the lessons of experience. For education this is an important fact, for the quality of the lessons written on the slate is crucial, since a child will use them to help him to think and to feel. The 'blank slate' notion needs some qualification. Certainly environmental stimulation is crucial but there has been startling evidence of the rapid tuning to faces and voices in a newborn baby a fact which suggests inborn capabilities. Moreover, intelligence and personality as every parent and teacher knows are not infinitely plastic and malleable though they are much more so than most physical and physiological traits.

Those areas of the cortex that are 'committed' from birth are vital to physical survival and are concerned with vision, hearing, touch and physical movement. Most of these areas gradually come into operation after birth.

Springs of life

Besides the cortex, which is largely taken up with higher abilities, there are more primitive, 'lower' centres deep in the middle of the skull and overlain by the great, convoluted cortex. These lower regions are concerned with basic functions such as hunger and thirst, arousal and attention, sexual drive, pleasure and pain and smell. They seem to provide the springs of life, urging us to act as we do. Some of these actions are assisted by hormones, chemicals secreted into the blood under the control of the brain. There is little doubt that most of our feelings and even decisions are at least strongly influenced by these parts of the brain and add emotional drive to the logical activities of the grey matter.

The automatic pilot

In addition to the cortex and inner core of the brain there is the cerebellum and bulb. The cerebellum, or little brain, lies below the back of the cortex and is second only to the cortex in size. It is corrugated by deep side-to-side ridges which increase its surface area. It is really an enormous computer which organizes body movements. Perhaps a better description of it is an 'automatic pilot'. It takes over actions merely sketched out by our conscious minds and arranges complex muscle team work to bring these actions about, so that a child can ride a bike automatically while using the cortex to solve an equation. Inadequate nutrition which affects the brain in many ways has a selective effect on the cerebellum in which certain structures are damaged; in animal studies this is associated with detectable though minimal clumsiness.

Alerting centres

Finally there is the bulb, the part of the brain-stem which continues the spinal cord into the skull. In it are centres for the control of life-and-death functions like breathing and the control of the tone of blood vessels. It possibly contains mechanisms which pick out the new and interesting while suppressing the less important, at a particular moment in time. 'This concerns you', the brain says and our attention is alerted. One can sleep through noise yet wake to a baby's cry. These 'alerting' centres may lie in the brain-stem but as yet there is no strong evidence that this is the only part of the brain which 'recognizes' these important signals. More evidence is necessary.

The hemispheres and teaching and learning

Our knowledge of the left and right hemispheres and their function provides some useful background to teaching and learning.[38] Both hemispheres are constructed identically yet they have different functions. The left hemisphere is usually associated with speaking, writing, mathematics and logic, the right hemisphere with spatial relationships, shapes, patterns such as faces and is concerned with emotion and intuition. The left and right hemispheres work together because, as indicated earlier, they are connected by a huge strap of nerves which ensures that both share in memory and learning. Such a connection also ensures unity of mental activity and behaviour. There is however almost total ignorance of how the two hemispheres work together and in what form information is transmitted from one half of the brain to the other. It might be added, for fear of misunderstanding that, it is very unlikely that 'logic' is safely lodged in the left hemisphere because, geometry for example must involve complex inter-relationships between both hemispheres.

One of the major themes of this book is the uniqueness of the individual and the need to maximize his or her potentialities. In this respect it is an important fact that each lobe of the cerebral cortex has its own rate of development, each area in each lobe (eg. for understanding speech or for remembering) also has its own rate of maturation. Moreover, each area shows differences in the rate of development of each of its layers, for the cortex is made up of a number of cell layers. Only the visual parts and those concerned with the act of speech show no great difference between one individual and another in their development at a given age. By contrast other areas show big differences between individuals at the same age and no doubt also between the fine 'wiring patterns' of the nerve cells within them.

To return to the hemispheres, a child's heredity determines which side of the brain becomes dominant but, with increasing age, specialization of the hemispheres begins and the 'spheres of influence' become established at about two.

For the past thirty years neuropsychologists have attempted to define the different processing strategies on the left and right hemispheres. Some divided people into 'artists' and 'thinkers'; artists with powerful right hemispheres who grasp the wholeness of things in a living unit, thinkers with dominant left hemispheres who attempt to split down reality into parts and later to seek to reassemble and breathe life into them. But people are not as sharply divided into holistic and analytic individuals as this. Most things children learn involve collaboration between both sides of the brain. Drawing, model-making, painting, listening to music are biased to right-side activity. Mathematics inclines to the left but spatial mathematics involves the right. Writing involves pattern and spacing (right side) and meaning (left).

As children grow older and specialization increases, the strengths of the right hemisphere tend to be increasingly neglected in education. *Primary Education in England* records that 'the standard of two and three dimension work in seven year old classes was generally more satisfying than in older classes and was consistently better matched to the children's abilities'. In secondary schools, particularly for the more academic pupil, aesthetic and practical subjects are usually undervalued, particularly after the age of 14, and the curriculum shows biases towards the academic and abstract. The Secondary Report emphasizes this point (see *Aspects of Secondary Education in England,* 1979):

> The more able pupils may have opportunities to take additional languages and separate sciences but may suffer from the loss of practical, aesthetic or humanities subjects and courses devoted to aspects of personal and social education. Whereas in the first three years all pupils within a school follow a broad programme covering all or most areas of the curriculum, the introduction of options in the fourth and fifth years leads to the abandonment of some important subjects and to insufficient breadth in some individual pupils' programmes

There is of course a discipline in dance, sculpture, painting, drawing, drama and music which is different from but equally as rigorous as that in mathematics and science.

With regard to the art and craft work of primary children, *Primary Education in England* states that

> The emphasis which has been placed on children using a wide variety of materials has in some cases resulted in children working in a superficial way. Children need time to familiarise themselves with the characteristics of particular materials and to acquire some degree of mastery over essential skills and techniques. A more carefully selected range of art and craft activities, worked at more thoroughly, would enable children to reach higher standards in the execution of their work and

obtain more satisfaction from it.

To watch children drawing or painting well it is obvious that the eye is in command and as a child matures his eyes are under moral pressure to reject the false and sentimental while the hand is under severe discipline to control line, colour, shape. Art, music and drama are not fringe activities but central to balanced development and the brain is starved without them. Indeed, it is true to say in this context that manual skills are just as important and unique in man as his language gift and fortunately the human love of working with hands is hard to curb, embedded as it is in our genetic make-up.

Reading

When a child starts to learn to read, his eye movement control system in the brain is suddenly called upon to perform at a very much higher level of precision than ever before. The eyes can deliver visual verbal material to left or right hemisphere depending on where they are pointing. Initially, however, only the left hemisphere containing the language areas can interpret what it is seeing. A child must learn to position his eyes very accurately when he starts to read in order to deliver verbal material preferably to the left hemisphere. The normal child achieves high positional accuracy for reading by developing a 'leading' eye; in other words perfecting the motor control of only one eye first.

Besides the fine eye-brain interaction referred to, to read and understand this page requires balanced activity between the two hemispheres because the right hemisphere recognizes the position and sequence of words while the clues to meaning given by the individual words are interpreted by the left hemisphere. When position and meaning are integrated by both halves of the brain the passage is understood.

When a young child stumbles on a difficult word he is likely to stick on that word rather than let his eyes rove a little way ahead to gain clues to meaning from the rest of the passage. If his eyes move from the word to scan ahead so that he can reflect on meaning, he might lose his place and the spatial activity in recovering it might jam the work of the left hemisphere which is trying to integrate the clues to meaning. The old method of marking the difficult word with a finger, then letting the eyes rove forward for meaningful clues, allows the eyes to return to the finger without effort; finger and eye work closely together automatically and the brain is not troubled in finding its place. In other words the finger is a solid point of reference so that the brain can reflect on meaning, as a walker who is lost pauses by some known spot to think, by a survey of the terrain ahead, which way to go. In relation to this Margaret Donaldson gives some sensible and practical advice on reading (see *Children's Minds*):

> A child will have the best chance of starting to consider possibilities of meaning if he is reading a coherent text which contains the right sort of balance between words he already knows well and words he is not sure about and if, further, the known and familiar parts of the text are so constructed as to guide him towards a manageable set of options when the unknown is encountered.

Scanning a text rather than stopping on individual words is a practice used by a good reader when he tackles a difficult text or foreign novel. He automatically breaks down a difficult passage into manageable chunks perhaps by right hemisphere activity but caution is necessary in giving too simple an explanation, for the left hemisphere must also be involved since 'chunks' tend to be marked by their order and meaning. The pauses in between the chunks help him to think about the author's meaning by using his left hemisphere.

A child (or poor adult reader) over-concentrating on individual words tends to miss the overall meaning of a passage, since it is possible that overactivity on one side of the brain blocks activity on the other side, though this is speculative. A child who is expected to respond to a flash card by making the right sound immediately to an isolated word will not be thinking about meaning; rather he will be 'barking at print', and under pressure, guessing wildly.

At a certain stage a young child can of course make progress by practising recognition and pronunciation of individual words without attempting to grasp the general sense. But soon he must be led to understand that the phrase, and then the sentence and even the passage, are in reality units which communicate the story which the author sets out to tell. It is not uncommon to find children in infant classes who can read the print but cannot say 'what the story is about'. This can be helped by reading the story aloud with the right cadence, and from an early age with the child in a comfortable position on a knee. In this way a young child can become familiar with the structure of language.

This kind of broad approach to language competence is tackled well in nursery and primary schools where teachers read and tell stories which range from traditional folk and fairy tales to modern stories of real life and fantasy. In many schools however one aim is 'to foster an enjoyment of poetry and literature and to get the children to think critically about what they have read'. Here the skills of a good reader need to be taught in the later stages of the primary school — to check, to scan ahead and look back. As the Primary Report states:

> . . . once the skills of decoding are firmly established further skills should be introduced. These include the efficient use of dictionaries and reference books, skimming passages for quick retrieval of information, scanning passages to establish the main points, the interpretation of context clues and the capacity to make sense of difficult passages.

The neurological evidence squares with this advice.

Girls and boys and brain differences

Finally, brain development in girls and boys is slightly different, and this may have a bearing on language development and probably on the early development of mathematical and scientific abilities in boys and girls. The speech areas in the left hemisphere are slightly more advanced by about two months in girls of four or five than in boys of the same age. Parallel with this the speech organs of girls are more advanced — on average they talk earlier than boys. In boys on the other hand, the right hemisphere is more developed and their capacity for spatial work with patterns and shapes is better, even from two. At about six in boys the right side is still advanced for spatial processing while in girls it is still not so specialized and, after accident to the left side, can take over the language function. On this evidence girls seem to have greater plasticity for a longer period than boys, perhaps up to 12 or 13.

These differences in brain development show up in the behaviour of nursery and infant children in particular. Girls between three and five or six become increasingly adept in talk and if speech is poor at home in these formative years girls may be disadvantaged because they are passing through a critical phase for language development. Most boys at these ages are exploratory but are not talking so much.

This exploring and experimenting may have a bearing on learning mathematics and science which in the early stages is not learned though talk but by experimenting and playing under skilled guidance with water, sand, shapes and so on.

Given time, boys can catch up on language (though girls continue to surpass boys in verbal fluency) but girls may not catch up so easily on play experiences that involve mathematical and scientific ideas. Probably we should stage-manage numerical, experimental and spatial activities for girls so they can learn much more through experiment, as well as through talk.

The need for balance of experience

Where does this kind of knowledge about the brain get us? It simply confirms good educational practice; neither side of the brain should be neglected, the abstract or emotional, but there is a tendency in later school life for the left hemisphere to be well cared for and the right to be starved — particularly with bright, academic children. A mind that knows only what is can express in words and numbers is parched and carries with it the danger of losing touch with the feeling of others and the solid reality of earth and body. It was A. N. Whitehead[39] who put this point forcibly in his essay 'Technical education and its relation to science and literature' when he wrote, 'in teaching you will come to grief as soon as you forget that your pupils have bodies', adding, 'It is a moot point whether the human hand created the human brain, or the brain created the hand'. Both boys and girls should have concrete experiences which give them plenty to talk about and which use the aptitudes of both hemispheres to the fullest extent. All young children need to have stories of quality read to them from an early age so that they will enjoy books and begin to learn that pleasurable experience can arise from print on a page. It should be remembered that reading is an active skill and the brain is an efficient scanner which naturally disposes children to learn how to read.

Chapter 8

The Maturation of the Brain and Vulnerable Periods in its Development

The growth of the mind depends partly on the maturation of certain parts of the brain and nervous system but it has to be admitted that we know very little about the links between physical changes in the brain and learning. The successive stages of mental functioning described by Piaget appear to reflect many of the features of the developing brain or body structures and the emergence of these stages is restricted by the gradual maturation and organization of the cortex.

Early brain development

At birth the infant's brain gradually comes into operation. The skin from all parts of the body begins to send messages to the brain in response to changes in temperature, contact with clothing and with the mother's body and arms, and, of course, all the effects of gravity begin to operate fully for the first time. The only movements that are obviously fully established at birth are the ability to breathe, to suck and to swallow, all of which are strongly activated for survival and are 'hard wired' in the brain, that is they can be done without teaching, while sucking and swallowing cannot take place at the same time

The brain comes to receive more information through the eyes than from any other sense, but what is first seen has no meaning, and all light is dazzling and discourages eye-opening. Hearing is very active, however, but the new noises of hospital or home may be disturbing.

Limb movements are limited and crude, and are hampered by the clothing required in cold conditions. Nakedness is obviously best for freedom of movement, but this may be limited by climatic or housing conditions.

Children differ remarkably from birth in the way they mature physically, mentally and emotionally. Each child goes through the same order of development but at different rates. Thus motor development (physical movement), language, social behaviour, and developments in thinking and feeling and in the senses unfold, at least in the early years, to some kind of pattern. In other words a child's capacity to walk, to talk, to learn and to respond to stimulation will all be determined by the maturity of certain nerve networks at particular ages. Premature babies for instance reach speech milestones at about the same time as babies born at normal time and stand and walk no sooner. There is much evidence that, in the brain, functions appear when brain structures mature and not before. As Tanner states, 'there is no reason to suppose that the truth of this generalization suddenly ceases at two or three or 13' (see *Education and Physical Growth*).

One point of detail which has been referred to previously is the relatively late development of the legs in man. At birth the motor areas in the brain are most mature in the region controlling the upper trunk, neck and upper arm, then the leg and hand and finally the head. By one month the hand has joined the rest of the arm and by three months the head has caught up and overtaken the legs. This order of maturity is maintained until about two. The leg areas of the brain catch up at about three with the areas controlling the upper limb and head. By this time (three) the infant is beginning to gain mastery over parts of his environment which he then uses to serve his own objectives. He is able to leave his mother to explore, a step in his final emancipation.

Similar unfolding of abilities happens in vision (see *Growing and Learning*). A baby of a few days old will track a moving light if the speed is not too fast and as early as two weeks can tell the difference between a grey patch and a square composed of stripes that are only one eighth of an inch wide, at a distance of nine inches from the face. At about four weeks certain parts of the brain (edge detectors) have developed which allow fixation on the most salient elements in a pattern — for instance on the face, the mother's eyes, because they have black and white contrast and move, or the edge, where the hairline meets the forehead. At about three months a mother's entire face is smiled at, not just the eyes. This is because the memory and visual parts of the brain have developed far enough to encode whole patterns and to form memory associations. The actual *understanding* of what a child sees gradually unfolds as the uncommitted areas of the cortex mature. Indeed as a general point it is possible that myelination of the higher parts of the brain, dealt with below*, may be very prolonged and associated with continually developing processes such as speech and abstract thought.

Early reasoning capacity of children

With respect to development of the intellect, a child may be able to reason before he is one. When something vanishes behind a screen, a one year old will probably know where it is, even though he cannot see it. This remarkable capacity of the baby and young child to 'reason' modifies some of the theories of the past about children's thinking. It is held by Jean Piaget that not until between seven and nine does a child develop powers of logical analysis (see also *Children's Minds*). It enables him to infer that if one thing is bigger than a second and the second is larger than the third, then the first must be bigger than the third. On the other hand if children of five or six are shown two sticks whose height is equal, but one further away than the other, they typically judge the further one as smaller. But children of four and five can reason deductively if the situation is a real-life one and not to do with contrived laboratory experiments. Observation of children in natural situations are likely to tell us more. Thus Margaret Donaldson cites comments children make and questions they ask when they listen to stories. Here are a couple of examples:

a. 'But how can it be (that they are getting married)? You have to have a man too' (The book contains an illustration of a wedding in which the man looks rather like a woman. The child thinks it a picture of two women.) (Premises: 1. You need a man for a wedding; 2. There is no man in the picture. *Conclusion:* It can't be a wedding.)

b. Child: 'You're not looking.'
    Teacher: 'Pardon?'
    Child: 'Why are you not reading it?'
    Teacher: 'Because I know it.'

* see page 76

(Premises: 1. When you read a book you look at it; 2. The teacher is not looking at the book. *Conclusion:* She is not reading the book.)

As Margaret Donaldson says, at least from the age of four, we must acknowledge that the supposed gap between children and adults in reasoning power is less than many people have claimed. Other modern work supports this view.

What is happening inside the grey matter to accompany these growing capabilities of the mind is unknown, except to say that the nerve cells in the cortex grow and form a rich network of branches from birth onwards. Perhaps the richness of branching of the nerve cells and their millions of interconnections are important in the development of intelligence. But for practical purposes a normal child of four or five has a brain which in certain circumstances is capable of thinking logically.

Progress, not only in intellect but feelings, is indeed a remarkable achievement in the first five years and a child entering a reception class has outstanding abilities. His speech is fluent. He loves reciting and singing rhymes and jingles. Also he likes to be read to or told stories and act them out later, alone or with friends. He understands the need for rules and fair play. He enjoys jokes and riddles and is tender and protective to younger children and playmates in distress and also to pets.

Development of memory

Memory is good. He appreciates past, present and future time. Indeed in the first five years the growth of memory signifies maturation of certain brain systems. At around eight months the visual cortex and the temporal lobes are able to discriminate between one pattern and another so that the face of mother can be distinguished from that of a stranger; with this comes a fear of strangers and 'separation anxiety'. This means that if a one year old is playing and his mother gets up and tells the child that she will be back shortly and then leaves the room, the infant will cry. Following the departure of his mother he generates from memory the 'model' of his mother's former presence and compares that with present knowledge (emptiness) in his active memory. But at this age he is unable to resolve the inconsistency. At three a child can talk with his mother and *understand* the message 'back later'. His active memory will integrate past and present experience and tell him that this has happened before and everything is alright and that she will be back. But mother must return to fetch him from play group or nursery school, or the memory systems and the models he is developing within it will give way to uncertainty and he will lose confidence.

Development of skills

To return to physical abilities: a child of five can hop, skip, climb trees skilfully and play all varieties of ball game with considerable ability. He can also move rhythmically to music, so that in the infant school at five he is ready to learn and perform a wide range of movements with confidence and grace, including the skills of throwing, catching and kicking. By four or five he is ready to paint and make things himself using a light hammer and a small coarse-toothed saw. His painting of black, yellow and red daubs is a Diesel rushing down the line to London and the two pieces of wood and bit of painted cardboard are a moon-rocket or Concorde. By doing these things not only is he developing physically but his language and intellect are growing. Language develops by doing.

Emotional development

Besides intellect, more subtle aspects of behaviour, feelings and moral judgments grow during these years. A baby smiles at his mother at around three months but real laughter, chuckles and squeals are present when he plays at six months. Amusement from a situation (such as a game of peek-a-boo) develops early at about $3^1/_2$ months, as Darwin[33] discovered a century ago in his investigations of emotion. Anger seems to develop at about four months and is marked by a red face and yells of frustration. Full temper tantrums are seen at about two when he is frustrated or trying to make himself understood.

Jealousy seems to arise at about 15 months. Charles Darwin first observed this when he pretended to caress a large doll in front of one of his children. Shyness arises later, at about 18 months, again observed by Darwin when he returned from an absence and the child he observed hesitated and lowered his eyes.

On moral judgement any parent or teacher will recognize how a child of six or seven knows that it is wrong to steal, to tell lies, to cry for nothing, and to fight. But he will not be ready to understand social injustice. But by nine to twelve he will recognize the injustice of a mother who will not allow her children to play with poorly dressed children, or of a teacher who prefers a pupil because he is stronger, cleverer, richer or better dressed. With regard to telling lies, children of 8-12 generally know that truthfulness is necessary for getting on together : (to the question 'Why is it naughty to tell a lie?' the child of ten answers 'Because you can't trust people any more' or 'Because if everyone lies no-one would know where they were'). Younger children regard a lie at its worst as being unbelievable; the older ones, on the contrary, condemn a lie in so far as it succeeds in deceiving the other person.[40]

Sula Wolff,[41] writing on childrens' reaction to death of a parent, states that their behaviour is as our knowledge of their mental development would lead us to expect. Up to four or five they ignore it or are puzzled by it and sometimes respond with a callous interest, but as Dora Black[42] observes, young children need to have their communications understood even when they are not yet verbal. So we need to be sensitive to their body language and their drawing and play if we are to help them. Judy Hildebrand[43] gives this touching example:

> John, aged four and Sally, aged seven, refused to speak at all during my visits, until I brought along a family of four dolls. They then fought over them, and finally both made the mother doll lie down; the children then became increasingly agitated and then threw away the two little dolls. At this point their father, who had been feeling very angry at being left to look after them after his wife's sudden death, had been talking of putting them into care. He had also insisted that the children could not possibly understand what he was talking about. I pointed out that the children in their play had clearly understood the situation although they could not express it in words; they were as angry and unhappy as he was at being abandoned and feared that he, too, would leave them.

Between five and eight children are fascinated by death and sometimes regard it as punishment for bad thoughts and deeds, and as reversible. But children should be given accurate information about death and allowed to participate in family grief. Sometimes children are deceived by being told that the dead person has 'gone abroad' and other fictions.

By about nine they understand the reality, and sorrow begins to be expressed in response to the loss of a parent. 'Before then', Sula Wolff writes, 'children often do not react emotionally at all or else they merely take a detached interest'. By ten or eleven grief is shown by fits of crying or withdrawn, apathetic or hostile behaviour because about then they know that death is irreversible and permanent and happens to each one of us. This is a subject which will be returned to in Chapter 16 for it is one which a school has to help a child cope with.

In passing it might be added here that the death of an elderly grandparent may be the first contact with human death for a young child. He will need time to ask questions but taking part in a funeral is a good way to stimulate curiosity and a search for understanding and knowledge.

All the above time-markers are of course only a rough ride to development. There is great variation in the way a normal child develops both physically, mentally and emotionally but the same milestones are passed more slowly in some children, faster in others. And certainly the growth of the intellect (the 'brain') is easier to chart than the growth of the 'heart' and courage.

Mind and brain

We might ask ourselves what is happening physically in the brain to accompany these marvellous developments of the mind. A few indications of developments have already been made but broadly speaking it is known that different parts of the cerebral cortex mature at different rates so that control over different muscles develops in an orderly sequence as a child learns to reach, stand, walk and talk. In all these complicated activities and in addition in the development of feelings, there are likely to be both inborn and acquired elements: that is specific happenings in the brain which are developed and matured by experience. The fine structures of the cortex, the nerves themselves, have to be 'ripe' before they can function and this is not achieved until the nerve fibre is covered by an insulating coat, myelin. In other words a nerve must have a myelin sheath before it can begin to 'fire' or conduct an impulse. Let us look at this in more detail in relation to maturation.

At birth the part of the brain cortex which controls physical movement (motor cortex) and the pyramidal tract part of the brain containing the nerve fibres which carry instructions from the level of the cortex to the motor nerves are not ready for action because the fibres are not myelinated. A few months after birth myelin has begun to be laid down in the tracts. This delayed myelination is not unusual; indeed it is an essential part of the child's survival kit.[44] As was stressed earlier, evolution has seen to it that a child must learn under tuition for many years. He must learn about the world by solid experience and experiment; to get to know the differences between up and down, space and solid, near and far by trial and error, learning so that he obtains a valid picture of the external world in which he can effectively move about before he acquires myelin in his pyramidal tract. Only then can he begin to experiment safely in his motor behaviour. Before this the parts of the brain controlling complex instinctive behaviour keep him kicking and squirming vigorously; but between the ages of two and four when the tract has myelinated, he climbs, jumps, rolls about, in short, explores and enjoys using his developing motor intelligence.

It is useful therefore to human learning that the sensory nerve fibres to the cerebral cortex which carry information from the eyes and the organs of touch, pressure, pain and so on are myelinated *before* the motor axons, since the motor system of the brain cannot properly control even a simple movement unless it knows where an object is and indeed where the hand is. A toddler reaches for his toy car. His eyes tell the brain where it is and the hand moves to pick it up. Even this apparently simple act is complex, for the brain monitors the movement of the hand ten times a second so that the approach of the hand to the toy is observed and any error corrected by the issue of fresh plans.[32]

In each of these continuously reissued plans which guide the hand to its destination the brain considers all the implications before action. He must not bang the toy down or it will break: 'careful', the brain says, 'go cautiously, remember what happened before'. As a child develops, the feed-back mechanisms of the brain allow quick adjustment to situations by the body. In ice-skating or gymnastics, split-second coordination is noticable in children of nine and ten.

The activity of the motor system, then, is initiated and controlled through its sensory connections. Indeed, the motor system is 'blind' without its sensory input and needs the guidance of experience.

Myelination of the higher parts of the brain may be very prolonged and possibly associated with continually developing processes such as social behaviour, speech and abstract thought. But it is here where ignorance outstrips knowledge.

Vulnerable times in brain development

Among the difficulties and complexities associated with brain studies one rather solid conclusion has emerged from recent experimental work: there are clearly periods during its growth and development when the brain is vulnerable to environmental insult. These environmental circumstances and their relationship to learning will be weighed up in Chapter 12; meanwhile what is the evidence for vulnerable periods in development? From the following three pieces of evidence it looks as if the plasticity and resilience of the human brain are remarkable and that although the periods do exist they are not sharp and clear cut but lengthy.

First, squint is likely to impair vision if it is not corrected in early childhood, and most squints arise between eighteen months and four years of age. Recent research has shown that the brain is vulnerable to the effects of abnormal vision up to the age of three. Squint affects vision because, if uncorrected, it results in the failure of the child and the future adult to develop full binocular vision with depth perception — that is, to appreciate objects in three dimensions. Depth perception depends on the proper nerve cell connections forming to link brain cells fed by one eye with those fed by the other. They have to be in balance. By three they are formed and damage to vision after the age of three is more difficult to put right if squint has not been corrected. There is some evidence now, however, that squints may respond to treatment even after the age of eleven[45].

Second, in the development of speech, discussed in Chapter 9, the child has an optimum time when his developing brain can master the skill of talking which forms an almost classical case of an optimal period. After about 12, a child suffering extensive brain damage on the left side (from a road accident) may be very backward in speech. After about 14 symptoms that remain five or six months after the injury may be irreversible. Nevertheless *permanent* loss of speech is very rare indeed in children and such data as are available suggest a remarkable capacity for recovery in teenagers after severe road traffic accidents. Schools may understandably take a very pessimistic view when a head-injured child first returns. But there have been quite remarkable recoveries and it is important that both parents and teachers do not have a pessimistic and set view of the consequences. Each case represents a diagnostic exercise that can only be solved over time as an injured child's response to the structure of a familiar learning environment is monitored and encouraged.

In cases of early damage to the left side of the brain, indeed up to the age of about ten, a new speech area can be set up in the opposite side of the brain. The young brain is very flexible, but seems to lose some of its plasticity (for speech) at around puberty.[46] In addition, children who have been kept in silence for the first dozen years of their life may be dumb or very badly retarded in speech (see the case of Genie in Chapter 9). In one city school, the head teacher told HMI of a child of three-and-a-half years who spoke only two words on coming to nursery school — 'tea' and 'please' (see *Growing and Learning*). When the head teacher tackled the mother about this, she said 'He doesn't talk, he has only just come to school'. The parent actually thought it was the school's job to teach him to talk. She had apparently not done anything for three-and-a-half years. That is an extreme example (and the child may have been abnormal), but it is the kind of disadvantage that has far-reaching effects on development.

Third, ethologists' observations and experiments with mammals and birds on 'affiliation' between mother and offspring shows that the bonding process may have to start immediately after birth (witness the lost piping of young ducklings). It is argued by ethologists and some psychiatrists that disruption of the early phases in forming the first personal bond between mother and human child is the primary cause of failure in children to form personal bonds with the mother and subsequently of social bonding of any kind. These bonds are formed and strengthened not simply by the presence of the mother or the mother figure (the blood-tie is not of prime importance), who feeds the baby but by an enormously subtle interaction between mother and child which involves eye-contact, touch (if a mother is left with her naked infant she touches each part of his body), the baby's cry, physical contact during breast feeding and facial expressions.

This delicately synchronized signalling and response between mother and child can be seen in the way a mother holds a baby, looks into his eyes, expresses mock-surprise saying 'ooooh' or affects the characteristics of a frown while the baby responds with his signals and signs — smiling, gazing, grasping, babbling. This interaction is often terminated by the infant looking away and initiated by the mother with a cue from the infant that he is likely to respond.[47]

In a human baby, however, attachment to one person, usually the mother, is likely to take place during the first year (the sensitive period) and not instantly, when the child is learning to discriminate. Indeed babies can attach to up to five people simultaneously and not necessarily always the mother, who is doing all the feeding and changing. This flexible attachment behaviour, in which a child learns that comfort and affection can come from several sources, has survival value (in an evolutionary sense) for such a child is likely to be more confident than a child who is afraid to leave his mother's knee.

These facts on attachment behaviour (like the other two examples of 'critical periods') have evolutionary advantage, for even after a 'bad start' in the first few months of life a child can recover and develop normal attachment behaviour, such is the plasticity and resilience of human behaviour. In fact broadly speaking the first year is a crucial time not only for forming a child's first love relationship which provides him with the basic security and is a foundation stone of sound personality development, but for developing a whole range of signalling abilities (smiling, crying, clinging and so on) that strengthen the bond between mother and child.

Needless to say, much more needs to be known about successful mothering and bonding behaviour. Experiences, both past and current, that help a woman to become a good mother, or those that make it more difficult, need clarifying. Does a woman's own experience of being mothered affect her ability (or lack of it) to be a successful mother?

Some mothers certainly have strong maternal feelings which enable them to achieve a firm bond of affection with their babies without difficulty, even after an initial period of separation. The strength of their maternal feelings may depend on the quality of mothering they themselves received in infancy.

In contrast, a mother may be unable to achieve this attachment without early close contact with her baby, and even then it may take a few days before the baby appears to her to be an individual and her own. Failure to form a normal attachment perhaps accounts for the higher incidence of "battered babies" among babies who were initially separated from their mothers for long periods and among the infants of mothers who were themselves deprived of maternal attachment.

Much more research is necessary on the importance of sensitive periods in development and in the growth, maturation and functioning of the brain. These straws in the wind from brain (and behavioural) studies do seem to indicate, however, that early experience is crucial in the development of the brain's capabilities. Early in life it does seem as if the brain's nerve connections are susceptible and become tuned to the influence of the environment and perhaps the brain loses its initial plasticity for speech after about 12 or even a little earlier. But this is *not* to say that the final pattern of nerve activity is settled by puberty; rather that certain pathways have been established and have emerged from haphazard activity of nerve cells.

The brain's resilience

All this evidence could be interpreted as depressing; it points to the crucial quality of early experience influencing the brain. An important question for education is whether a bad start is irreversible. The picture is not yet crystal clear but considerable evidence[48] is accumulating from a variety of sources that the brain can catch up, given proper stimulation even after early adversity. To quote one piece in a little detail: Jerome Kagan, Professor of Child Development at Harvard has produced some convincing facts on the plasticity and resilience of the human brain in *The Growth of the Child*.[49] Kagan found that children in certain Indian villages of Guatamala were kept in dark huts and were hardly spoken to or played with for most of the first year of their lives.

Moreover their health was poor. Despite all this they were loved and wanted by their parents. After 12-18 months the greatly retarded children left their huts and were allowed to explore and encounter the rich variety of the world. By the age of eleven they had not caught up with eleven year old American children but by late adolescence their retardation had faded and the majority of them were gay, alert and intellectually competent children, almost as good as children who had grown up in more varied and challenging settings.

The important conclusion from the evidence available seems to be that the human brain does have the capacity to catch up after a bad start but if a child continues to grow up in poor, unstimulating surroundings, if his bad experiences are cumulative, there may not be much hope of catching up. This is the 'wedge hypothesis' which suggests a greater potential responsiveness during early life and childhood at the thick end and tapering off to less responsiveness in adulthood, the other end.

Relevant to a major theme of this book that the critical time for rapid learning is from birth to puberty the Court Report states:

> We now know that the effects of early disadvantage can be much diluted by the environmental circumstances the child encounters during the middle and later years of childhood; and that it is especially worth making this corrective effort because early disadvantage tends to lead to later disadvantage, so that, unless there is intervention, there develops a compounding of difficulties. It is this train of events which is influential rather than the critical effect of particular circumstances in early life considered in their own right.

This robustness and resilience of the human brain in its ability to recover from adversity is an encouraging one for foster and adoptive parents. It must be stated, however, that in some of the evidence, for example in case studies of isolated children, it is impossible to be sure what the outcome for these children might have been if a favourable early environment had been available. In other words a child of 15, seriously deprived until aged three and greatly retarded in growth and backward, with an IQ of, say, 80, might have had an IQ of 140 if he had been reared normally, in which case he is still very seriously retarded.

The effects of early adversity highlight especially for schools the importance to each and every child of a firm, caring environment where individuals are valued, feel they will be listened to and where grown-ups can be trusted. It also means in the early years of schooling a curriculum and a level of expectation which recognizes that a five year old who is normal can think, is physically skilful and can use language well. The curriculum itself needs not only to provide stimulus and new experiences but to capitalize on the everyday experiences of the children themselves. The importance of the interdependence of school and family needs no stressing. The family serves as a secure base for most children from which a child can test out his world and which helps him to establish standards. When a child is older in the junior and secondary years there is a need for the home to support the learning at school.

Chapter 9
The Gift of Speech

In Chapter 7 it was pointed out that the brain seems to search for clues in the environment that help to explain it. The brain does not scan haphazardly but seeks to test some hypothesis. Similarly with speech: something is developing in the brain which helps to analyse regularities in language, see order and use old words again in new combinations never heard before.

Marvellously, children the world over begin to speak between their eighteenth and twenty-eighth month just as naturally as they begin to walk. Indeed language development up to about four is sufficiently regular to represent the unfolding of inborn potentialities guided by heredity. Its milestones are synchronous with other physical developments like stance and gait and though its onset is unaffected by environmental deprivation, the language gift soon shows signs of impoverishment in the disadvantaged. After 12, as Chapter 8 indicated, the brain, as far as language development is concerned, becomes set in its ways. In this respect it is interesting to note that during the early years of language acquisition, the organization of language may be easily modified in almost any way; that is any language may become a child's mother tongue if he is adopted from one culture into another at an early age. By 12 or 13 it becomes more and more difficult to learn a second language though of course not impossible (see *Speech and Brain Mechanisms*). But it is important to stress a general point here, and one emphasized by an example on p.84: that the brain remains resilient in all sorts of ways well up into the twenties, thirties and forties, if practice continues.

Though the human brain is very robust in the face of environmental abuse we need to make sure that the unique human quality of speech and language learning is not neglected in the early

years of life. Puberty is time-tabled by the body glands of children
and we expect and allow for it. We need as well to plan the curriculum
to adjust to the unfolding capacities of the brain and seize on the best
times for language learning.

Language deprivation

That language, like food, is a basic human need without which, at a
critical period of life, a child can be starved and damaged, is a lesson
that Emperor Frederick II of Sicily in the thirteenth century taught
us. His cruel experiment with foundlings was designed it is said to
discover what language a child would speak if he heard no mother
tongue; he told the foundlings' nurses to maintain silence. Before the
first year was out all the infants died. Clearly there was more than
language deprivation here. Good mothering which embraces a
sensitivity to a child's needs including language development was
missing. Without good mothering the capacity to survive is
drastically affected despite good feeding and clean conditions.

A good number of modern studies seem to indicate that the
human brain can weather early neglect. The story of Genie[50], an
American child, is worth giving in detail to illustrate the resilience of
the brain and the capacity of a child to speak after severe deprivation.
From the age of 20 months until her admission to hospital at 13 years
9 months in 1972, Genie suffered terrible deprivation — isolated in a
small, closed room, tied to a potty chair where she remained nearly all
the time, sometimes all night. If she made a sound she was beaten.
Her father and brother never spoke to her but barked at her like dogs.
Her mother was forbidden to speak and allowed to spend no more
than a few minutes with her during feeding. Genie was a prisoner with
no language for the eleven crucial years between two and puberty. But
marvellously she can now speak simply through exposure to talk. She
is of course backward — at 20 she talks like a two or three year old,
but understands much more. Her progress is slow and it is uncertain
how far it will improve. Moreover as well as developing language,
Genie can take a bus to school and has begun to express some of the
basic human emotions.

The story of Genie also underlines the astonishing resilience of the
brain: as Jerome Kagan[49] puts it: 'the mind may have some of the
qualities of an elastic surface, easily deformed by shearing forces, but

able to rebound when those forces are removed'.

Just as health and survival appear to depend on good mothering so do all other aspects of child development including language development. The mother's method of teaching language is the direct method. It is the same in all lands and its methods are commonplace. The mother talks to the child before he can understand. Before he speaks she is on the lookout for understanding. When he says his first words he is egged on by an admiring audience. Language for him is direct. He uses it to get what he wants, to understand facts about toys, animals, books. He uses language, not as an end in itself, but to learn about life and to share his ideas with others. The learning of the mother tongue is an inevitable process. No parent could stop it unless his child was placed in solitary confinement, but the language gift can be squandered by shut-down answers and lack of stimulus with books and toys and play. The inevitability of language learning is strikingly shown by two Danish children brought up by their deaf mute grandmother in a remote area of Jutland.[51] The children conversed fluently in a language which no one could understand and which had no similarity to Danish!

Language and brain development

The evidence of linguists and neurobiologists suggests that speech milestones are reached in a fixed sequence which differs from individual to individual. There are cases, particularly in boys, where speech has started very late in a child who proves to have a high IQ. At 12 weeks a baby smiles, coos and utters vowel-like sounds; at 12 months he can speak single words — 'mamma', 'dadda' and understands simple commands. In these early months there is an enormous push to mastery of language, pleasure where communication succeeds, and also great resistance to frustration. In the second year it is clear that the child's understanding is developing rapidly but speech lags. There can be a lag of two to seven months between first hearing and utterance. Between two and four baby talk vanishes and is replaced by adult pronunciation. It has been suggested that by four half his intellectual growth is over, a growth as great as that of the next 13 years. At any rate by four he has attained considerable knowledge of the grammatical system of his native tongue. And this stunning intellectual achievement is routinely performed by every pre-school child. Some set of structures in the brain is developing that can scan the environment from infancy to discover from the hubbub some kind of order in language. When a child is six he is ready to expand his vocabulary rapidly. As he passes the age of nine the process is accelerated. From a vocabulary of 1,000 words at three he can pass to 10,000 using the same language set because the sound, pronunciation and spelling are similar, though usually his accent still resembles that he was first brought up with.

But what is happening inside the brain up to the time language breaks through at about two? And what happens between then and about twelve when the brain appears to lose its plasticity with regard to language learning?

All that can-be described are structural changes. Nothing is known about the causes of language development which might have a biochemical base beyond the scope of our present tools.

What can be described, is the nature of the brain differences before the onset of language and after the basic language skills have been acquired. Even though these observations are crude they at least tell us something about the changes in the solid stuff of the brain as it matures and thus about the substrate of language, memory and mind. The most dramatic fact is the swiftness of brain growth during the first two and a half years of life when vocabulary is increasing fast and the brain reaches 75 per cent of its adult weight. By about 10 the brain has reached adult weight, and speech is firmly established in the left hemisphere of the brain. As already explained the fine structure of the brain is developing rapidly in the first two years of life. The billions of nerve cells in the cortex are growing and branching to form a dense web of interconnecting branches (see fig. 1, pp.42-3). The timing of nerve cell development is interesting. Microscopic examination of certain parts of the cortex, as referred to earlier, show a dramatic increase in branching of nerve cells between fifteen and twenty-four months. It is as if the brain is building up to a springboard of nerve development from which speech can take off. Before this period, at about one year, language development is hampered by the sheer immaturity of the brain. The difficulty is 'cerebral', not in motor ability. Thus words can be babbled involving complex movements of the larynx, tongue and lips[52].

Detailed examinations show that the parts of the cortex controlling the power of motor (spoken) speech (Broca's area) and also the memory ('association') areas develop fast in the second year of life. But ahead of the development of these parts of the cortex are the areas which involve vision and hearing and between these, Wernicke's area concerned with understanding speech. Both Broca's and Wernicke's areas are in the left hemisphere (see Fig.2). These observations tie up with the fact mentioned earlier that a child learns to understand first, then to speak. They also help to explain the fact that by four, language is well established because the underlying brain mechanisms of understanding and speaking are more or less perfected and act synchronously.

The association areas mentioned above are very large in man and represent brain tissue available for information storage and retrieval. In other words they are stores — a treasure-house filled with the sounds and sight of words — which can be combined to generate myriads of utterances. Clearly it is useful to man as a speaking, thinking animal for language to be developing and interacting hand in hand with the parts of the brain concerned with memory, vision and hearing. The information store allows past memories to be scanned before decision and is a valuable human asset.

Finally, to add to the picture of the silent machinery that channels thought into language, the brain even from birth appears to be built to absorb language rapidly. Wernicke's area — the speech region that lies in the upper and posterior part of the left temporal lobe — is bigger from birth than the corresponding region on the right side. So not only observations on the development of speech milestones but brain shape suggest that before any environmental effect such as language teaching, man is born with a pre-programmed biological capacity to process speech sounds; or in other words with a brain poised to learn speech at birth.

The special nature of the human brain

Clearly, from what has been said, man's brain is 'special' compared with that of other primates and it is advantageous for those concerned with education to be aware of its special features. It is not merely a bigger version of an ape's brain; its basic wiring patterns for the production and reception of speech are very different. The parts of the brain devoted to vocalization and control of articulatory muscles cover about one quarter of the motor area of the brain in man. The same general order of parts is observed in a monkey but they cover only about one tenth of the motor cortex. Sheer size of brain does not matter either, for there are people, dwarfs, of under two feet high, whose mature brain weight is only a third the size of a normal adult, yet, though backward they can speak as well as a five year old[53]. Brain size is not important for speech but the wiring patterns are.

These are profuse and cross-connected and enable children to connect the sight and feel of say a cat, with the sound pattern 'pussy'. These cross fibres are so numerous that a special switching mechanism, the 'superassociation' centre, has evolved just behind the temple which facilitates connections between the areas of the brain concerned with sight, touch and sound[54]. In a monkey the visual and auditory areas of the cortex are connected by very few nerve fibres. There is therefore little opportunity in the monkey brain to learn to associate an image and a sound.

A child sees a black, furry, oddly-shaped, moving thing. He recognizes that his mother couples the thing with the sound 'pussy'. The concept is 'recorded' as previously mentioned elsewhere in the memory areas as a 'concept-unit'. The associated sound is recorded in the speech area of the left hemisphere as a 'sound-unit'. When the two units are established with their nerve connections, the child understands.

Depending on whether he likes or is afraid of the cat he cries or smiles. But the next step must be taken. He must speak. Egged on by his parents he imitates 'pussy' over and over again until he gets a perfect 'verbal-unit' recorded in the left hemisphere. Exactly how the memory is recorded is a central problem in physiology. But we know that what we pay attention to is recorded by nerve mechanisms in certain areas of the brain, described in Chapter 7. On the other hand, what we ignore leaves little lasting trace in the brain. Something more than the mere passage of a nerve impulse is involved in the recording of the memory trace — here in this instance the speech-units.

Thus when a child starts to understand, he is laying down concept-units in the memory areas of the brain and corresponding sound-units in the speech area. When speech starts to burst through rapidly at two or three, he has established 'verbal-units' in the left hemisphere. Perhaps the verbal-units (or put more simply 'word-formation units') help to bring into play the set of muscles used to pronounce the word. The child makes a better and better unit by experimenting with the word 'pussy' ('pooty'), trimming it and refining it, helped by approval and by appearances of the real cat. This is why we hear the delightful word experiments of a child. He needs to experiment — and be encouraged to experiment — to sharpen the verbal unit in the brain. As speech develops the blank slate of his speech mechanism that he was born with soon becomes filled with units. After ten or eleven they can hardly be erased though they can be added to, but with increasing difficulty.

Wilder Penfield's[46] idea of sound, concept and verbal 'units' may be entirely plausible but in fact there is little hard data at the moment to support their existence as physical structures in the brain. A 'perfect verbal-unit' implies a very specific programme in the brain for producing a specific word but this is too clear-cut for an instrument as flexible as the human brain. To emphasize this flexibility, a motor movement, such as a hand sign, may be produced in response to a great variety of sensory stimuli. In later life for a child simply to see pussy does not necessarily evoke the word 'pussy'. Rather because of the interconnections of the speech and memory areas, 'pussy' might summon up a whole collection of relevant detail. Human memory and learning in fact, thrive on complex 'associations'. Say any word and a whole pool of memories and associations are stirred, different for each person. In short, we do not think or remember in a rigid, slot-machine way and specifically, with regard to speech, the *whole* brain intervenes between what is seen or heard and what is uttered as speech.

Traditionally speech and language were thought to be located only in the thin skin of tissue, the cortex, the human thinking cap, but deeper parts of the brain are involved. The 'finding of words is made possible by the left hemisphere of the cortex working with a small mass of tissue, the thalamus, just below it. Many speech disorders too may have their roots in deep and mid-brain structures.

The quality of mothering

Speech has to be triggered in the brain which is poised to learn language and it is here that the quality of mothering and early teaching is crucial. The quality depends on the mother's sensitivity to the cues and signals or 'sign language' of the infant and child. The mother needs to recognize the signals in the child's babbling, clinging,

grasping, crying, smiling and respond to them in appropriate ways —
the bonding behaviour as described in the last chapter. Insensitivity
of a mother to a child's signals dulls the interaction and can keep it on
a concrete level because the child gets discouraged and sends out only
the obvious signals. Sometimes, as Daniel Stern[47] has described so
vividly, a mother may misread a baby's signal or else respond
inopportunely so that sometimes she will 'chase' and the infant
'dodge' trying to break visual contact by pushing his face further into
the pillow or by closing his eyes (see *The First Relationship: Infant
and Mother*). Sensitivity of a mother to the child's non-verbal cues,
correcting and regulating the interaction, stimulates greater and
greater levels of communication between them, giving the richest
opportunities for the growth and development of language and
indeed other capacities. A successful mother will believe that
children of less than a year old are capable of taking initiative and
sharing joint enterprises. An unsuccessful mother tends to think of
children as passive and without initiative. The former is more
successful in generating communication; the other less so.

When a child is older, a mother needs to recognize the signals
implicit in how he stands, the way he uses his hands, his eye
movements and facial expressions, for a child's looks and behaviour
convey meaning. Of course the way a mother interacts with her child
is not studied but is done 'without thinking'. Nevertheless, as Charles
Darwin[55] noted 'the force of language is much aided by the expressive
movements of the face and body. We perceive this at once when we
converse on any important subject with any person whose face is
concealed'.

When a dull or retarded mother or simply and more commonly, a
distracted, tired mother interacts with her child, she is not sufficiently
sensitive to his signals. Failure to observe these keeps the child's
development on an obvious, dull, concrete level.

The environment, too, affects this interaction. Take malnutrition:
one of the first effects of bad feeding is reduced responsiveness of a
child to the environment. The interaction between the mother and
child is dulled: the value of the child as a stimulus to the mother is
reduced and this may serve to reduce her responsiveness to him.
Apathy breeds apathy and the end result is significant backwardness
in intellectual capability.

There is then supporting evidence for sensitive periods to back up that given in the last chapter: as far as language development is concerned, the human life span is likely to have in it periods when man is highly sensitive to learning language (and may be other skills like playing an instrument). The years from about two to twelve appear to mark the start and finish of a period characterized by a rapid burst in language development up to about four then a slow approximation to the final state. Up to two, language is held back by the physical immaturity of the brain. After about twelve the brain loses its flexibility. But within the span of years two to twelve, the years up to age five are crucial, for the brain is growing fast and its fine wiring patterns are developing and forming subtle and rich connections. The brain may be so plastic at this time that the visual and sound environment might cause irrevocable biases in the wiring patterns, though as yet there is no evidence for this in man.

The language environment

A good language environment is as important to the development of the brain as fresh air and good food are to general health. First, a successful parent — mother or father — will believe that a young child is capable of understanding and sharing joint enterprises. A baby drinking his milk is talked to by his mother in sentences, 'Yes, it is nice, isn't it? Would you like more?' The baby goes back to his milk and the mother believes that he has understood. Only by these tiny assumptions about understanding and intelligence does the baby begin to develop these qualities. Later, a parent needs to make an effort to understand a child's meaning when he is playing or helping in the house, and to help him express himself coherently rather than dismissing a jumble of words as nonsense. Children who have had this kind of cooperation make good listeners and talkers.

Second, it is a basic characteristic of the brain that its nerve cells repeat patterns of activity and future skills such as walking, talking, or writing are developed from these earliest patterns. Complex skills like these can be used again more easily once the nerve pathways have been formed. As the brain works on repetitions it is important for language development to repeat words, phrases and songs and in addition to associate pleasure with repetition — warmth and comfort while listening to a story is a strong booster to learning, during the pre-school and infant stage especially.

Third, 'shut-up' answers, in place of dialogue can harm the

development of language. There is encouraging evidence from the
Primary Survey that in most primary schools children's vocabulary is
steadily extended. In many schools children are encouraged to
elaborate and explain answers or comments and are helped in this
way to find more precise and appropriate ways of describing what
they have seen or experienced. There is often a 'good level of noise' in
a primary school that strikes the visitor, easily distinguished from
disorder. In the last analysis, however, children learn to speak from
their parents and while some children enter school with meagre
language development, others have a rich vocabulary. The job
facing the schools is how to close the gap as soon as possible, for gaps
widen and those boys and girls who sit bored and often tucked at the
back of the class at the age of fourteen are often those who entered
school with poor language development. *Aspects of Secondary
Education* is critical of what secondary schools are doing to help
children express themselves orally, particularly the average and just
below average pupil. Nevertheless good examples are described.
Thus:

> One of many interesting examples of successful discussion took
> place during work on a CSE Mode 3 English syllabus in an
> urban comprehensive school. Nearly all of the pupils
> contributed detailed accounts of street play experiences, the
> teacher sustaining interest by unobtrusively leading them to
> focus on detail. It was this detailed recall which gave life to the
> descriptions and held the interest of the whole group for more
> than thirty minutes. The value of the teacher's restraint,
> coupled with his unforced interest in the individuals and what
> they had to say, was confirmed towards the end when one boy
> (by no means the most articulate) asked the teacher for his
> contribution. It was willingly given, and conveyed the same
> pleasure in personal recollection.

Fourth, the homes that children come from have what might be
called a 'hidden curriculum' of the home — important in language
development. Some parents organize their children's environment
with an educational aim in mind, through books, talks and visits, but
their children may not have had sufficient rough and tumble play or
experience of messy activities. A four year old child from a bookish
home may know all about lenses, magnets, thermometers and so on
but will suddenly turn into a baby and roll about the floor babbling.

He or she may need to regress from talking to tipping, filling, dabbling, climbing and running. Other children know the life of the streets and are not short of group play and language experience to discuss, as shown above. They run errands, have their gangs and street games, help dad to build a pigeon loft and go to football matches and whippet races but they may lack the massive 'back-up' from homes of books, of explanations, opportunities to learn new words, and so on. Many of these homes are certainly not uncaring. Other children live in rural poverty and some in isolation but may know a good deal about trees and wildlife, soil, rocks, farm implements, machinery, birth and death. Others from rural situations may be very deprived linguistically: father and mother may be involved in a harsh work regime and the child from his early days may have been put in a pram in the corner of a field, and at three or four may be playing on his own.

Fifth, perhaps schools and play groups need to 'compensate' for deficiencies and adjust to the individual child's needs with appropriate experiences. Children who live in rowdy public conditions need quiet areas in which to learn to read quietly, to paint, to listen to stories. Children from urban back streets need to experience more living and growing things in schools, and to talk and write about them and paint them.

Some children's imaginative potential is stifled by parents who are matter-of-fact and who may over-supervise their reading and think that imaginative play — with its associated language is silly. But children like funny exaggeration and do not believe all they read or hear. These children like all others need good stories, dressing up and play experiences to light up their imagination.

Children who live in isolated farms and in hamlets need to experience co-operative activity in art, science and so on which brings with it language and social interaction. *Individual* needs are stressed because generalization about disadvantage seems unprofitable.

Sixth, many parents of pre-school and primary children think they cannot help in the learning process, including language development, but they often make the mistake of thinking that it is necessary to be complicated. There is good evidence from the Primary Survey that children's own experiences frequently provide the basis for language work in school. Thus three-quarters of seven year olds and nearly three-fifths of the older groups wrote and talked about animals, plants or about things to be seen within the school. It is the detail that attracts children: looking into the mouth of a foxglove flower, watching a caterpillar cross the yard, an ant bearing its load or a magnet attracting a paper clip, seeing a Slow Worm, examining a modern painting, are all wonderful experiences, just as much as are dressing up and role play. As the child 'behaves' in these situations he acquires language to match but the situations have often got to be created ('stage managed') to make children use their brains and imagination. For an adult to help it is important for he or she to:

> To see a world in a grain of sand
> And heaven in a wild flower
> Hold infinity in the palm of your hand
> And eternity in an hour.

Seventh, in the development of language, imagination and a child's senses and motor skills, toys are of course of great importance. Toys should be chosen which catch and hold a child's attention, provide repetitive experiences and stimulate a variety of exploratory activities. They need to have strong colours so that a child can learn to dinstinguish them and should come in a variety of sizes so that the meaning of big, tiny, medium-sized can be understood. Shapes should be provided, and objects that fit together. Not only the senses can be used by listening to the sounds toys make, how they feel and what they look like, but motor skills can be developed by pushing, pulling, building, fitting together and so on. As toys are used with the mother, language grows, conceptual ability expands (red, blue, green are all colours) and imagination blossoms — his brick house becomes a castle and himself a giant.

Eighth, it is important too not to destroy the silent pleasure of looking, smelling, feeling and listening, by too much well-meaning interference with books, explanations or silly questions.

Chapter 10

Play and Learning

Susan Isaacs called play 'Nature's means of individual education. Play is indeed the child's work and the means by which he grows and develops'. This thought is not always understood by parents especially when a child first starts 'proper school' at five. Some parents grumble because they think that their child is playing about too much and not 'working'. Play is hard to define but it is a collection of activities through which a young child learns. In playing, a child grows in intellect, in his emotions and in his moral sense; and it is quite likely that the drive to play is inborn and coincides with the long childhood from birth to puberty mentioned earlier.

Starting school

The first day at school is a major event in the lives of all children and the parents who take them. Old people of 70 or so often remember the day, the teacher and the smell of the classroom, it is so impressed on their minds. Most children settle in well because schools make them welcome and see to it that they are busily occupied and happy. It is not only the first day that is crucial but the first few minutes, and a sensitive teacher will adjust her expectations to the needs of the individual child: one needs great security, another might stand and look at the Home Corner and then gradually be encouraged to join in the activities there. In a village school a child will meet only a small number of other children of his age and the experience will not be so bewildering as in a big school. Even so, in small or large schools, a child's world suddenly changes and with it his daily routine. Playtime can be frightening but a small child in an infant class usually has his own playtime, not with bigger junior age children. There are rules to keep to and a different pattern of life from home.

A few children even by the end of the first term have not settled. Martin Hughes and Gill Pinkerton[56] say that about one in eight show some anxiety, have temper tantrums, lack concentration and have some difficulty in sharing after a term. Some of these have very specific difficulties such as lack of coordination in using a crayon or with the use and understanding of speech. More boys than girls show these difficulties. Most upsets soon vanish but they will be eased if, after the first visit to the school of a mother with the child, a close association between home and school develops which is helpful to a child's progress. This mutual understanding ensures that neither home nor school make conflicting demands and the relationship between play and learning is understood by parents. Of course, good organization helps to make starting school a smooth transition. Children are usually admitted at the start of each term but if small groups can be admitted, spread over a few days, as is the practice in many schools now, then each group can be initiated gently into the ways of the school. Other organizational arrangements are common but more important than these is the ethos of a school: the way teachers speak to each other and to the children and the value they place on their individual efforts will create the atmosphere which, for better or worse, children will surely sense.

Play and learning

Children of all ages learn in many ways, of course, not only by exploratory and imaginative play but also by imitation and from games with strict rules.

Soon after birth a baby will start to explore his mother, himself and his surroundings with his eyes and will gradually learn to move his toes and fingers and to reach out for objects; all this is exploration — getting to know the properties of something. Children also learn by imitation, that is by translating perceived into performed movements. At 18 months a little girl 'reads' a book, sweeps the floor, kisses her doll and powders her nose in imitation of her mother. When older, a child needs good models to imitate and these are necessary in a family.

Games, like hop-scotch, marbles and Cowboys and Indians

provide another kind of play in which children learn skilled movement; they also learn that they must stick to the rules of a game or it will not work — by these means they learn the essence of morality.[57]

> It is a pleasant sight to see the young play with those of their own age at tick, puss in the corner, hop-scotch, ring-taw, and hot beans ready buttered: and in these boyish amusements much self denial and good nature may be practised. This, however, is not always the case. (The Boy's Week-Day Book 1834).

In all these forms of play children develop physical skills as well as their powers of thinking, speech and feelings and the ability to order and control them.

Children also learn by sheer absorption of facts, by learning by heart which they love, and, when they are older, by absorbing other people's opinions. The exploratory drive is however a powerful antidote to mere rote learning and passive acceptance of other people's views. Maria Montessori[58] and others, who base their views on close observation of how children learn and how they fail, advocate less absorption of 'knowledge' and more 'self-activity'.

In a young child play is often serious and absorbing; he really lives his role. To watch a child of three acting out the mother and child role tucking up a doll in bed, talking all the time about what she is doing, or to see infants dressing up as brides and grooms or doctors and nurses, will underline the serious attitude of the child to some of his forms of play. Many kinds of play of course are not serious and children play for fun — bouncing a ball, spinning a top with colours chalked on its top and so on.

Niko Tinbergen, the ethologist, observes that in all animals most of the learning is left to the young themselves; although a mother cat will take a live but incapacitated mouse to her kittens, it is left to them to use the mouse to practise on (see *The Importance of Being Playful*). Much of our own behaviour has animal roots but our own particular forms are unique and depend on our large brain; and also on the fact that in contrast to that of other animals the human brain is open and flexible, with its behavioural instructions sketched in only lightly by heredity. Thus, from an evolutionary point of view, one basic importance of play is that it provides the growing child with practice in a variety of behaviour patterns on which inheritance has given only slight guidance.

A good home, play group, nursery class and primary school provide a fertile environment for a growing child to play and learn in. The functioning of play groups, nursery and primary schools cannot be understood without a knowledge of play and its basic importance to learning. They provide opportunities not only for a child to nourish his mind and develop his language and imagination but also to explore relationships with other children and to exercise his body. Many of the activities of course embrace all these at the same time.

Exploration

There is very much still to be discovered about how the mind works and about children's play but it seems that children at all stages of development from birth onwards try to make sense of the world in their own way. In the very early stages of learning children must see, hear, feel, taste and smell things in order to find out what they are. Never again will they depend so much on these senses. They cannot learn simply by being told and even at age one appear to learn by experiment. Niko Tinbergen recorded these observations about the exploratory learning of a one year old:[59]

> A 12 month old boy, guarded by his aunt and grandmother, was observed crawling over a sandy slope which was bare but for isolated rosettes of ragwort and occasional thistle plants. After having moved over many ragwort rosettes without showing any reaction to them, he happened to crawl over a thistle, whose prickly leaves slightly scratched his feet. Giving a barely perceptible start, he crawled on at first, but stopped a second or so later, and looked back over his shoulder. Then, moving slightly back, he rubbed his foot once more over the thistle. Next, he turned to the plant, looked at it with intense concentration and moved his hand back and forth over it. This was followed by a perfect control experiment. He looked round, selected a ragworth rosette and touched it in the same way. After this he touched the thistle once more, and only then did he continue his journey.

This description is a highly sophisticated example of true experimentation in a pre-verbal child. What the child was doing, and of course what all children try to do, is to apply the scientific method to the environment. A child has to learn the nature of things by experience; he then draws his conclusions which he tests, just as the child did going back to touch the thistle and the ragwort.

This way of acquiring knowledge of the world through trial and error is the basis of all later intellectual activity. For all young children throughout the primary phase of schooling, interest can be aroused and stimulated by creating an environment which invites exploration. It is very likely but not proved that exploration has its effect on the brain and physically changes the nerve connections in the cortex.

A good environment for play includes several ingredients. Security is important, for a child will not play if he feels abandoned or in a strange place. Adults must know the right time to intervene; too much joining in or too much taking the lead, may, like too many toys, hamper exploratory play. Structuring of the environment with definite objectives is important and necessary and is of course practiced by many teachers.

There are obvious constraints to play. A hungry or sleepy child will not play well, neither will a sick child or one who is worried by home problems. Exploration is probably the most powerful and direct way of acquiring information and learning; perhaps in other forms of play learning is more incidental.

As children grow older and enter the nursery and infant years, exploratory behaviour seems to unfold. A three year old finds out that he can construct bridges when playing with blocks. He experiments and learns the essentials of cause-effect relationship: beating a spoon on the table makes a funny sound. He makes jokes: a carefully built brick tower is suddenly knocked over with glee. He imagines when he plays pretend games; when he rides his trike it becomes a space ship. Because he is a very immature personality he feels with enormous intensity and his play can be used to act out and to help him to control his feelings. Maggie Tulliver in *The Mill on the Floss* kept a wooden doll in the attic which she punished for all her misfortunes . . . 'three nails driven into the head commemorated as many crises in Maggie's 9 years of earthly struggles'. A three year old might smack his teddy which symbolizes his mother who seems to be neglecting him because of the new baby, or simply because the child wants to be naughty himself and dare not be.

Play and language

Language in the four to five year age group progresses by leaps and bounds. A four year old has several thousand words at his command and his activities help him to develop language strongly. For example, children taken to see a suspension bridge want to build a bridge 'just like the one we have seen'. After much trial and error and repetitive play for several days they are able to produce an interesting group of bridges spanning various kinds of roadways and intersections and the good teacher encourages them to use the correct words for bridge and road construction. Their experiences have been profound: they have felt different kinds of bricks, experienced light and heavy, rough and smooth, sensed the effect of gravity. They have looked at houses and cranes and vehicles and talked about them. They have learnt new words and had experiences of sorting and ordering. All through this type of play they have discussed and asked questions. Their thinking and language obviously grow as they play but also, less obviously, they learn to cooperate and share and control the rages felt as someone takes the brick they were going to use. Toys were mentioned in the last chapter as being important in the development of language. It might be added here that a good toy can help in learning to solve problems. Thus the door on a toy car should have a special way of being opened, not just by pulling and should stretch the child's ability so that he moves from the familiar to the unknown.

Language has in addition an enormous value as an instrument of playfulness. Children enjoy fooling with words thinking up odd combinations of animals and animal sounds — the dog clucks and the cat chirps. They like absurd rhymes — the cow jumped over the moon; or incongruities — the blind man gazes, the deaf man listens; or slips of the tongue — the man bit the dog on the leg. Such absurdities strengthen the child's sense of reality and do not upset his stability. A child of two or three can know a language joke and enjoy it, provided that he understands the true conception of reality which he can compare with the false.[60]

The need for skilled planning

A visitor to a good primary school or play group will realize that behind the informal atmosphere and purposeful noise lies a backbone of skilled planning. There is nothing haphazard about the organization. In an infant class of seven year olds or a class of ten year olds the right materials need to be on hand for the various activities. Books and other materials need to be there to choose from. The teacher needs to be aware of individual differences and decide when each child is ready to learn something new. There is direction and stage-managing of activities by the teacher, based on clear objectives, detailed planning and on a sound knowledge of the individuals in the class and their needs. A brief example shows this awareness of development. Many primary schools use mathematics in display and this helps to foster a lively interest in the way numbers work. Thus in a reception class display can be used to show the number of people living in a house and later on at nine, the relative size of the planets.

The teacher will know too what each child has done in the day so that a record of progress can be made and his future programme planned accordingly to develop his language, number sense and imagination.

Sometimes, as stated in the report on *Primary Education in England,* opportune use is made of spontaneous incidents to encourage exploration. A good example of this was seen in a class of seven year olds where the teacher had introduced a topic on water, following the interest aroused in the children by a burst water main outside the school gate. In the course of the work, children examined a number of different aspects of the subject including rusting, floating, sinking, water levels, rates of flow, the importance of water to plant and animal life and the source of their own drinking water. The work involved discussion, writing, drawing and practical experiment and culminated in a visit to a local reservoir. In this case the teacher used a combination of straightforward factual teaching and exploratory approaches. Occasionally she followed up a point of interest raised by a child and sometimes she presented the children with a practical problem to be investigated.

Games were mentioned earlier in this chapter and Iona and Peter Opie suggest that children like games in which there is a sizeable element of luck 'so that individual abilities cannot be directly compared. They like games which move in stages, in which each stage, the choosing of leaders, the picking of sides, the determining of which side shall start, is almost a game in itself' (see *Play: its role in development and evolution*). The development of a sense of fair play, tolerance and a spirit of reciprocity can be prompted in' playing marbles for example. If a change is proposed in the game 'some want

to and some don't. If boys play that way (allow an alteration) you
have to play like they do'; and 'sometimes people play differently.
Then you ask each other what you want to do . . . we scrap for a bit
and then we fix things up'.

Brain and mind

A few facts seem to stand out from close observation of children's
play.

First, the progress of development appears to depend partly on
maturation of certain structures of the brain and partly on practice.
Thus the ability of a child to build a tower of bricks requires
maturation of his cortex but practice also plays a part. Speech
depends upon the development of brain structures but also upon
listening to others and using words.

Second, it is clear that a child's exploratory behaviour and play are
basic inherited drives and start very early in life. Much of the activity
seen in primary schools, nursery classes and playgroups takes
account of this so that under skilled guidance a child can instruct
himself for a good proportion of the time.

Third, the early years of learning (from about two to seven) are
those which Piaget called the 'pre-operational' stage of thinking. This
stage is crucial to the next, the stage of 'concrete operational' thinking
which spans approximately the age range seven to twelve (see
Chapter 14). By 'concrete' Piaget means *thinking* about doing things
with physical objects: ordering, classifying and arranging them in
series by visualizing in the mind's eye, groups of bricks, dogs, cats,
flowers and so on. By 'operational' he means actions (not of body but
of mind) such as ordering, separating and recombining. The 'pre-
operational' stage of thought depends very much on the actual
physical experience of touch, sight, smell, hearing. Thus a child who
has gone shopping with his mother, helped with home chores, played
with bricks, sand and water, and has had experience of exploring his
'near' environment of home and garden will before five be preparing
his mind for the concrete operational phase. At the infant stage the
experience of the actual will be strengthened by the kind of activity
described in this chapter.

Piaget described the child's mind in the pre-operational stage of
thinking as like a slow-motion film, representing one static frame
after another but lacking a simultaneous encompassing view of all

frames together. In other words a child's thinking at this stage is a succession of separate views of things so that he is unable to reason out the relationships between them. Thus a child of five or six may judge two children to be of equal weight when standing but not when one of them is seated. Ask a child of three or four to group similar objects from a mixture of several sets of coloured shapes and he may at first choose a blue triangle and a blue square because they are the same colour but then he will add a red square because it is the same shape as the blue square and then revert to colour by choosing a red triangle. Children of four or five will make drawings, as Jacqueline Goodnow in *Children's Drawings* observes, which rely on one unit as a reference point for an adjacent one, rather than considering a group of objects in their entirety. When they crayon in their 'News Book' a washing line and a house, they work from one item to the next rather than considering the whole pattern. At this age a child often makes a drawing of his way to school with the houses at 90 degrees to the road and the chimneys a neat 90 degrees to their immediate reference point, the roof. Only when they are older, at eight or nine can they cope with multiple relationships and think of the chimney as related to the roof and the ground. Drawing and painting help to make children's thinking visible.

Children at this pre-operational stage seem to make logical decisions but find it difficult to justify them and change their minds quickly if the criteria which helped them to arrive at a conclusion 'change', as the examples mentioned above show.

Piaget's hypothesis, that children cannot reason at four or five, has however been modified as Chapter 8 showed. It seems that children of this age are not so limited in reasoning power as was once thought, as witnessed by their devastating logical comments when listening to stories. Even with contrived experiments, Peter Bryant [61] showed that five year olds can combine separate experiences and reason from them providing they can *remember* the information which has to be combined. When errors occur they are due to memory failures. All this evidence shows simply that children's powers as thinkers in the infant school must not be underestimated.

Further chapters will continue to discuss the growth of a child's mind, but just how a child arrives at the concepts of classification, sharing, comparing and reversibility is unknown. Though experience is of course crucial, it seems as if the brain is maturing to enable a child to combine distinct experiences in new ways. This is unsatisfyingly vague but at the moment we do not know.

During a child's years in the infant school the rapidity of his learning and development generally in two or a little under three years is little short of a miracle. His powers of language, both oral and written, at the 'top infant' stage are remarkable. Written work can be produced in great variety: news, stories, poetry, descriptions. Sometimes lengthy stories with chapters are written. Most can read, many with fluency, having in a couple of years learned to extract meaning from the 'marks on the page', itself an outstanding achievement. Their knowledge of shape, size, number and quantity will have taken firm root, grounded in solid practical experience. They can paint and use many kinds of materials and tools.

Socially a seven or eight year old is self-possessed, responsible, independent and capable of getting down to a straightforward task in a practical and determined way. These stunning achievements are accompanied by the swift growth and development of the brain as described. In these early years and indeed right through the primary school, a child burns brightly, living with the quick intensity of a young animal.

Memory and teaching and learning

The ideas already posed about the experience of exploration and play can be linked with another important idea about brain development previously referred to. This is the development inside the cells of the brain cortex of a symbolic 'model of the world', 'composed of hypotheses about the world and later used to decide upon programmes of action that maintain life' (see *Programs of the Brain*). Throughout life the brain model (or our memory system) is enlarged and added to and becomes highly personal because of different individual experiences.

Memory of course is of key importance in the model because information has to be stored somewhere and, as described earlier in Chapter 7, new information fed into the brain through the senses must be scanned against experiences stored in the memory areas. This scanning is an important process, because before a decision is reached and action is taken it is likely that the brain areas involved work towards answers by running through a series of sequences of operations that are something like the situation that now confronts them. In other words, hypotheses are tested by small-scale 'experiments' which go on inside the head. If experience says 'test further', as with the exploring child touching the ragwort and the thistle, then action or decision follows. All the time through language, imaginative play, imitation, games, books and instruction, the model of the world inside the head is growing and being refined. The stored information then makes up our 'model of the world' and the whole aim of education is to provide a model which is flexible enough to cope with the situations that confront it — to make sensible decisions and forecasts. Knowledge of the exact nature of the model is vague as yet. The enormous task that lies before science is to show how the brain cells provide the code in which these hypotheses and programmes are laid down.

If the memory system is a device which helps us to make accurate forecasts for the future and so helps us to 'survive', no explanation is forthcoming about how brain chemistry and physics rapidly produce scenes from the past in all their brightness, colour, detail and emotional content[62], how as George Moore wrote poignantly:

> Fond Memory brings the light
> Of other days around me
> The smiles, the tears,
> Of boyhood's years,
> The words of love then spoken
> The eyes that shone
> Now dimmed and gone
> The cheerful hearts now broken

Teachers and parents will, however, recognize three aspects of memory which are important in teaching and learning and another which seems surprising.

First, as Jerome Bruner[63] said, perhaps the most basic thing that can be said about human memory after a century of intensive research is that unless detail is placed into a structured pattern, it is rapidly forgotten. In other words if the material to be recalled is unrelated, such as a string of random numbers, a child will remember much less than if the material is connected as in a story or a sentence. In doing this the brain is exercising one of its normal protective functions which is not to take in things that seem of no use. To remember everything would be an embarrassment.

Second, a child may learn or is capable of remembering only those things to which he pays attention. None of the things he ignores appears to leave a memory trace in the brain. In other words only when a child is focussing the spotlight of his attention on this or that is he writing on the brain's slate. Only what is relevant and interesting to a child is likely to be remembered. This idea needs to be capitalized by providing plenty of opportunities for exploratory and imaginative play and good models to imitate.

Third, the brain's capabilities, including memory, seem to be impaired by anxiety. Anxiety, especially about home conditions may cause some children to suffer from 'school phobias'. These children are not primarily frightened of school but feel, with good reason, insecure at home. John Bowlby[64] provides convincing and often horrifying evidence that children who refuse to go to school have powerful reasons for remaining at home. They believe understandably and sometimes correctly that their parents may abandon them if they let them out of sight, or may drop dead or be unbearably lonely while their child is away at school. Parents who enforce discipline by threatening to leave home or commit suicide are far from uncommon. Many children sense too that their insecure mothers are pathetically dependent on them. These inadequate parents retain the child at home to be a companion. One effect of all these anxieties is to impair concentration and memory.

The surprise: it seems as if children's immediate memory for the information presented in a story is higher first thing at school (at 0900) than in the afternoon (at 1500) but that delayed (one week) retention is superior following presentation at 1500 hours.[65] The 0900 superiority of immediate memory is found to be largely confined to relatively unimportant information. In contrast, the superior delayed retention following afternoon presentation is unaffected by level of importance.

Whatever physical base for memory exists in the brain, the model of the world created in the brain cells must depend on the quality of experience a child gains through his sensory system. It has been stressed throughout this book that the developing human brain is extremely flexible and open compared with the brain of other animals and that heredity has left man with but vague instructions for most behaviour including his greatest gift, speech.

In other words the brain is not so genetically 'hard-wired' as was once thought. Most behaviour is learned by trial and error, by imitation, by playing alone or with other children or with adults. On the other side of the coin, simply because the young brain is so open and impressionable it can be damaged, by producing a state of mind

which expects little out of life. Eleven words quoted in a recent book*
on the brain sum up what the message of this chapter is — 'A good
environment is not a luxury, it is a necessity'.

Programs of the Brain J.Z. Young, Oxford

Chapter 11

Accidents

Accidents can happen anywhere, at any time to people of any age but children are particularly at risk since accidents of some sort are part of the learning process. Between the ages of one and fourteen accidents are the commonest single case of death. In this age group the house, the playground, the road are all potential hazards. Every child stands a 1 in 16 chance of being injured in a road accident by the age of fifteen.[66]

A child under five should never be far from an adult. Many of the accidents that he becomes involved in are the result of his normal and relentless desire for experimentation, play and adventure but it is foolish to leave him playing alone.

Separation anxiety

Much evidence suggests that a child up to about three needs a close link to an attachment figure, usually but not always his real mother[64] (see Bowlby, J. op.cit.). After about three, when a child can understand that his mother will come back, he is ready to leave her for short periods to go to school or playgroup or be with someone else whom the mother trusts. Animal and human studies show that fear is aroused in situations which are in themselves harmless but which signal an increased risk of danger: one of these situations is separation of a child from his mother. Evolution during thousands of generations has engineered this attachment behaviour which requires a child to be in close proximity to special companions. It is safer like this: accident statistics show that young children left alone are vulnerable. A young child becomes anxious when his mother disappears even for a short time simply because by being alone he instinctively feels less secure than when with someone. A child may cry in these circumstances. Crying in more primitive conditions helps a child to be found and saved. It is part of a survival kit inherited from a different and fiercer environment shared with other primate species.

Non-transport accidents

For the under fives most domestic accidents (see MacFarlane, A. op. cit.) happen, surprisingly, in the living or dining room, about one fifth in the kitchen and large numbers in the bedroom and outside the house. Most are falls from furniture — chairs, beds, tables. Next come accidents on stairs, trapped fingers and falls from windows. Third are accidents with kitchen equipment — teapots and kettles, wringers and spin-driers. Poisoning is a rare cause of death but enormous concern and anxiety is caused by accidental poisonings. Every year about 16,500 children under five are admitted to hospital in Great Britain suffering from suspected medicinal poisoning (see *Prevention and Health*). The following story is illustrative of many episodes.[67] A professional man recently brought his two children to hospital with aspirin poisoning (which incidentally, with paracetamol, was involved in about half the cases of suspected poisoning in 1973). He and his wife were upset less by the poisoning than by the fact that they had tried to teach the elder boy aged three never to take any tablets out of a bottle. So much had they trusted him that they had knowingly left the aspirin bottle by his bedside. This episode illustrates many points relevant to child poisoning: toddlers are usually the ones affected, parents often have unrealistic expectations of their children's behaviour, the poisoning although occasionally not serious nevertheless produces a lot of anxiety in most cases. The use of child resistant containers will cut down this number of poisonings as their use becomes more widespread. Indeed the latest research in Wales and the North East shows that the number of children admitted to hospital having taken overdoses of aspirin and paracetamol — two drugs now sold in special containers — is now one-fifth of what it was before the containers were introduced.

Deaths of children from non-transport accidents follow, as expected, the pattern described above. Among pre-school children by far the largest number of deaths in the years 1968-74 occurred at home (66 per cent boys, 76 per cent girls) in contrast with 22 per cent of fatal accidents to boys and 53 per cent fatal accidents to girls of school age (MacFarland, A. op. cit.). Tougher glass in doors and safer window catches are necessary safety measures.

Accidents in quarries and industrial premises accounted for 10 per cent of the fatal accidents to boys aged 5-14 years, but only 2 per cent of those to girls in the same age-group. The percentages of fatal accidents to this age-group which happened in places of recreation (dealt with in a moment) were very similar for boys and girls: 10.5 per cent for boys and 10.6 per cent for girls. More boys than girls die in accidents, however, and this disparity increases with age. Taking risks is part and parcel of the male evolutionary equipment. He has to try his own courage. Disobedience in the face of reasonableness is normal.

A Nursery Rhyme[68] full of odd contrasts but subtle meanings is pertinent to quote here:

Three children sliding on the ice
Upon a summer's day
As it fell out, they all fell in
The rest they ran away

Now had these children been at home
Or sliding on dry ground
Ten thousand pounds to one penny
They had not all been drowned

You parents all that children have
and you that have got none
If you would have them safe abroad
Pray keep them safe at home

Road dangers

Road accidents are the major cause of death in children up to 15. Most (70 per cent) are killed as pedestrians, pedal cyclists (13 per cent) or as passengers in cars (13 per cent) according to accident statistics collected between 1968-1974.[69]

The factor which above all others affects the chances that a child will play in the street, run errands, ride a bicycle on the road, walk to school on his own, is his age. Nothing apart from his age seems to influence the mother in letting him do any of these things for her or for anyone else. Nevertheless among those killed playing in the street in the December quarter of 1978, 34 were under fives; 79 between five and fourteen.[70]

If children of nursery or primary age are asked what they are frightened of and why, half of the three to seven year olds and a third of the ten year olds will say that they are most scared on their way to and from school 'because of the traffic'.[71] To judge the speed of cars and the complexity of the traffic environment is very difficult for a small child. And of course when the attention of small children is diverted by the sight of a friend across the road, or even by a thought, they become so taken up with their feelings that everything else ceases to exist for them and accidents often occur for this reason. No child in the vulnerable age group of four to eight should be out in the street alone and the limitations of the young child and his normal stages of development should be understood by parents and by future parents.

The younger the child, the greater is the responsibility of the parents to guard against the inevitable accidents of all kinds that happen to all children at some time. Whereas the younger child must be protected as much as possible from accidental injury, the older child must be taught to protect himself. Children need to be taught the habit of crossing on zebra crossings and to understand and respect traffic signals. Children also need to be set a good example in traffic, because they imitate actions rather than listen to explanations. It is important too to see that bicycles are in good order and not to let children out on bicycles alone before the age of nine. In the last analysis however it is adults who are to blame for child accidents. Drivers need to be taught about the behaviour of children in traffic. Other hazards are bad planning of busy roads near schools and the shortage of play grounds protected from traffic and of pedestrian ways separated from car traffic. Road safety campaigns appear to be paying off, however.[72] In 1971 in England and Wales some 11,000 children were killed or seriously injured on the roads while walking or playing; in 1977 just over 8,000. Some 2,500 cyclists under 15 were killed or seriously injured in 1971; in 1977 about 2,000. Boys are more at risk. Twice as many five year old boys as girls were killed in 1977. Despite the improved statistics each death or serious injury is a family tragedy and current accident statistics leave no grounds for complacency.

Although children of all ages need somewhere safe to play, the difficulties are particularly acute for families with children under five — a fact reflected in the accident statistics just mentioned. A recent study in Newcastle[73] found that although the majority of mothers who had been rehoused from a slum clearance area found their new flats an improvement on their previous accommodation, 64 per cent with more than one young child felt that the move had had a deleterious effect on their children, and older mothers found the strain particularly intolerable. Even where play facilities were provided, these were unsupervised and 30 per cent of the under fives never used them. Those who did could only do so when accompanied by an adult or older brother or sister. Most children had to play in the bedroom or living room, and risk disturbing neighbours with their noise.

Mothers also expressed a high degree of anxiety with regard to safety, both in the flats where balconies, windows, lifts and stairs all presented potential hazards, and outside where play equipment was often unsafe and many play areas were near busy roads.

Playgrounds

Accidents as just implied also happen to young children in playgrounds. One recent study[74] showed that climbing frames and slides are associated with more severe injuries than swings or other equipment. The youngest children are at particular risk on equipment such as the wooden rocking horse or roundabout where the speed of operation can be controlled by older children. Many of the injuries to the very youngest children occurred when they were walking behind a moving swing. Faulty equipment does not seem to be the major factor in causing accidents but rather the use by older children of apparatus designed for younger ones. In over half the cases where accidents occurred an adult was about. As would be expected many accidents were due to normal childhood rashness — walking on top of a climbing frame or turning somersaults on one, pushing others off a slide or swing, standing on the swing, or even standing on the shoulder of another child on the swing. These activities could hardly have been prevented and are the result of the normal desire of children for experimentation and adventure.

Accidents are the most common cause of injury in the western world today and for over 25 years they have been the commonest single cause of death in children aged one to fifteen years in the British Isles. While they cannot be eliminated completely prevention of the most severe should be the aim. A recent booklet concludes with the following statement:

> It may sound paradoxical, but we do not expect, and do not even aim at, a national reduction in the total number of accidents. The vast majority of childhood accidents result in minor injuries. They are to a large extent unavoidable and even desirable from the educational point of view. We do not want to

restrict the child's normal and free development of behaviour by trying to shield him from many types of accidents. What we are striving for is to prevent serious types of accidents and potential causes of disability or death. Even a very good result within this limited scope would only slightly reduce the total number of accidents but it would bring about a further reduction of childhood mortality and disability and this is what we are hoping for.[75]

This seems to be a realistic and sensible approach and one that needs to be supported.

Chapter 12

Is the Young Brain Vulnerable to Adversity

It might be useful to draw together some of the factors referred to earlier which may reduce the brain's capabilities. Disadvantage, in an educational sense, is provided by an uncaring home devoid of love that affects a child's mental, physical and emotional development. Disadvantage in this sense has of course, little to do with economics. A 'poor' home in the economic sense may have plenty of affection, talk and things to do and may also provide a child with the ability to solve problems. The Court Report had this to say about disadvantaged children:

> Children who grow up in poverty or squalor, whose homes are grossly overcrowded, or who live in decaying inner-city neighbourhoods; children who are neglected or handicapped, or who are discriminated against on grounds of race, language, colour or religion; children whose parents are sick or psychiatrically disordered, who quarrel incessantly — or who are absent; such children are in different ways 'disadvantaged'. The term has no precise meaning, but the implication is clear enough. Social or personal disadvantage is handicapping and dysfunctional. Of course many children who are disadvantaged personally or socially may develop normally and function adequately. But they face greater odds than other children: they are more likely to suffer from physical illness or psychiatric disorder, or to fail educationally, or to drop out of school or be 'early leavers', more likely to truant or become delinquent, or to leave school for unemployment or poorly skilled jobs.

Indices of disadvantage

Classically the kind of disadvantage described exists in its concentrated form in the city slum. In lesser concentration it exists on bleak housing estates in town and country, in rural cottages, on isolated farms and also in polished homes in commuter belt country.

In a physical sense the infant mortality rate and the height of children at a given age can be used as a measure of disadvantage, provided that it is understood that both measures are considered in relation to averages of groups of children rather than for individuals in whom allowances have to be made for hereditary differences. Broadly speaking, differences in nourishment and care influence both. Over-crowding, dirt, poor food and bad housing, a father out of work, ignorant parents and broken homes send up the average mortality rate. For many of the same reasons, the average heights of children of manual and non-manual workers show a two centimetre gap at three and a five centimetre gap at adolescence. While most urban communities contain a mass of disadvantaged children, infant mortality and height indices are related more closely to social class and availability of facilities than to 'town' or 'country'.

Disadvantage and the brain

None of this physical evidence tells us much about the effects of neglect on the intellect, and knowledge on this subject is sparse. There are, however, certain environmental influences which are likely to hamper brain functioning and development. Although these are given separately, each is difficult to isolate as a cause of low intellect and poor character, for most belong to a syndrome of poverty and of course to heredity.

a. **Chronic malnutrition** harms the brain. Both before and after birth the developing brain is hungry for protein. The brain is beginning to grow really fast in the last three months of pregnancy and in the first two years of life and this spurt may be a once only opportunity to build the brain properly. In other words chronic bad feeding and especially shortage of protein during pregnancy, in the suckling period and in the first two or three years of life are likely to harm the brain and intellect. In addition mothers who have starved through pregnancy (as in some countries of the Third World) produce a smaller child at birth with the risks spoken of earlier. Malnutrition in 'rich' countries, however, seems to reduce human achievement markedly only when it is added to other adverse factors. The effects of poor feeding need to be looked for later when a child is at school not only for its effects on physique but on the energy available to learn. Many school children, compared with those of previous generations, stay up late and have a late evening meal with parents who have often both been at work during the day. As a result children may not be particularly hungry in the morning and a proportion set off to school having had little or nothing to eat or drink. A survey of school children in the London Borough of Brent[76] recently showed that a substantial number of children, regularly came to school having had no breakfast (4 per cent infants, 9 per cent junior, 21 per cent senior). By mid-day some children will have fasted for 16-18 hours and are unlikely to be alert during lessons. Not only no breakfast but poor breakfasts with high starch and sugar content cause tiredness and lack of concentration by mid-morning; but good protein breakfasts, egg and toast, cornflakes and milk, sustain energy by keeping the blood sugar up. The brain is the principal user of glucose under normal conditions: 38g per day at birth, 99g at five, 108g at ten. The breakdown of this glucose by oxygen (which the brain uses avidly) yields about 20 watts per unit time — the electricity necessary to light a dim bulb — yet the brain's potential kept going by so little energy needs no description.

The Working Party[77] on Nutritional Aspects of School Meals, reporting in 1975 recommended that a school meal should provide a minimum of one third of the recommended daily intake of energy and between one third and one half of the recommended daily intake of protein. They reported that 'we do not think it safe to assume that all children receive a satisfactory diet at home'.

Needless to say most cultures seem to have natural food combinations which give a balanced diet and provide all the essential protein necessary for sound growth. In this country it is virtually impossible to have an unbalanced diet (unless one becomes a food-faddist) because of the variety of food available. Immigrants however may be used to foods and climatic conditions which are very different from those found in this country. Some may arrive in poor nutritional health and continue to eat food which may be inadequate particularly in pregnancy. The traditional diet in Asian communities, for instance, is low in various nutrients especially protein, iron and Vitamin D and can lead to low birth weight babies with the attendant dangers spoken of earlier.

b. **Smoking heavily** (10 or more cigarettes a day) seems to increase the risk of having a baby with low birth weight, who will grow to a smaller child than average and possibly be backward in intelligence. There is some evidence that heavy drinking is harmful for the same reasons.

c. **Lack of opportunities for exploration and play** and its associated language development may damage the mind as much as smoking damages the heart and lungs. 'Shut-up' answers to questions, lack of dialogue and of opportunities for broader conversation, such as family meals, may hamper brain development as may harsh work regimes on isolated farms where children are alone for long periods. In rural areas, isolation from language and from other children may be significant factors in hampering human achievement, though generalization is dangerous. A mother in a city may be as isolated in a tower block and if the lift breaks down her small child may be deprived of play with others and of opportunities for play and language.

d. **A poor start in family life** affects general development, intellect, and emotional and social progress. Although, as emphasized in earlier chapters, most school children are healthy and have caring homes, many live in divided or broken homes, in poor houses and overcrowded conditions. In Great Britain in 1976 there were about 750,000 single parent families (10 per cent of all families) with 1,250,000 dependent children (1 in 15) (see *Social Trends*). The majority of these families result from breakup of a marriage and about 90 per cent of them are headed by a divorced or separated wife. Nevertheless the increasing number of remarriages may mean that lone parenthood is often only a transient status. Then there are many families who live in physically unsatisfactory conditions: overcrowding, poor housing and sharing. Almost 3 million families in England and Wales were in this plight in 1976. Bad housing, of course, can exacerbate an already tense family situation. Indeed a study of children who had been battered by their parents found that many of the families lived in very bad housing, most of it

privately rented and concluded that the conditions had
certainly contributed to 'non-accidental injury'. Fortunately
however, housing conditions are improving. Very few
children[72] for example (about 1 per cent) live at third floor level
or above in blocks of flats but play space nearby is often poor
and dangerous. Many housing estates are bleak with little for
children to do.

Perhaps the bad effect of separation on a child brought up by
single or divorced parents has been over-stressed. Where break-
up of the marriage or partnership is preceded by long discord,
the behaviour of the child can be adversely affected; less so
when a parent is lost through death. In plain terms family
discord may be more damaging to a child than separation,
though in a one-parent family the male or female model is
absent. A father's absence, especially if it happens in the first
five years of a boy's life, can affect his concept of masculinity.

The Court Report sums all this up:

> there is now extensive evidence that an adverse family and
> social environment can retard physical, emotional and
> intellectual growth, lead to more frequent and more
> serious illness and adversely affect educational
> achievement and personal behaviour.

It is hardly surprising that a study of slow learners[78] in
secondary schools in 1967/68 found that adverse social
conditions were widespread among these educationally
retarded pupils.

e. **Lack of sleep** may be another adverse factor. Sleep may be
important to give the brain 'the rest it deserves' after the
immense barrage of information fed into it in the day, but the
amount of sleep needed is variable and a child is only not
getting enough where it is tired the next day. Some
physiologists claim that those nerve cells which are the seat of
intensive activity during the day and where chemical change
goes on need to recover. In short sleep may be a period of
maintenance and repair of the nerve cell networks used in
memory and learning. In the young, where new synapses are
being formed and the wiring of the brain is changing, sleep is of
very great importance. Though there is a lack of hard
information we all know from experience that 'sleeping on it'
helps to clarify and consolidate thoughts.

f. **Noise** which can reduce sleep and concentration may affect the brain though this is uncertain; children can enjoy noise and commotion and 'switch off' when need be.

g. **Anxiety** as indicated earlier, may also affect memory and concentration. There can be in school an anxiety to please, to give the 'right' answer in class, while worries about home conditions (such as mother threatening after a row to run away or commit suicide or a parent whom the child thinks is unbearably lonely or depressed) can lead to school refusal when the child is afraid to leave the mother in case something may happen to her. Disturbed or delinquent behaviour can also result.

h. **Pollution of the environment by lead** in air, dust, food and water, in paint and cosmetics is under suspicion as being harmful to the brain. It is known that lead is a dangerous nerve poison and its effects differ among individuals but symptoms of lead poisoning are vague: headaches, depression, lassitude, anxiety and loss of appetite. Children may also develop disturbed behaviour and become backward in school work. It will be clear from this list that it would take an extremely perceptive doctor to disentangle these symptoms from the ordinary stress of industrial streets, poor housing and inadequate nutrition.

Special concern has been voiced about pollution of the air by exhaust fumes which are a source of lead. No report or study has, however, satisfactorily established a causal link between atmospheric pollution (from exhaust fumes), blood levels of lead and educational attainment, hyperactivity and other disorders.[79] In fact the major source of lead in the blood is food and not the atmosphere. Children living in cities who are not specially exposed to lead derive 55-95 per cent of their blood lead from food, 0-40 per cent from water and 3-10 per cent from air. The weight of evidence suggests therefore that environmental lead, most of which comes from food, soil and water and not petrol, seems not to have a major effect on the intellectual or behavioural development of children but at high lead levels there is a possibility of subtle impairment of fine motor or perceptual skills.

'Adventitious' lead, from old lead-containing paint (a small paint flake 2-3mm in diameter may contain over 1,000 ug of

lead or over ten times the daily intake from all other sources)
lead coated toys and lead containing cosmetics and medicines,
can harm more than petrol fumes and priority needs to be given
to preventing children ingesting paint and using these
cosmetics. Vigilance is necessary too, to identify toys for sale
which are coated with paint containing lead in excess.

Further research is clearly necessary to clear up the doubts
left about the relationships between exposure to lead and
intelligence, educational attainment and behaviour in children,
since other countries, Sweden for example, are considering the
adoption of lead-free petrol after reports concluded that there is
a link between lead levels and the impairment of city children's
intelligence. The Swedish evidence follows that from West
Germany and the United States.

i. **A 'bad start' in babyhood** and the first few years must also be
included. But it may not be so harmful to later development as
was once thought provided that adversity does not continue
through the formative years from birth to puberty.

Minimal brain development

Weighing the evidence on how these separate influences may affect
the brain, it has to be admitted that opinion and speculation are
involved. Perhaps the brain's capabilities are reduced only when all
or most of the factors mentioned above impinge on a child for a
lengthy period. Moreover, despite the depressing catalogue even the
worst slum, the meanest apartment, the remotest cottage should all
have the basic raw materials for some intellectual and emotional
development.[80]

Thus, a child needs to hear people speak, for the brain is poised to
learn speech at birth: and all normal families talk.

Next, the child needs to imitate, to explore and play in order to
develop his feelings and intellect. The brain is finely tuned and is in a
two-way dynamic relationship with the environment within days of
birth and seems to strengthen its powers by practice. Thus a child
needs from birth an environment containing objects and stimulation:
even the poorest tenement flat and the meanest backstreet has these
things — shapes, colours, things to play with. But the tower block
often denies access to play space or garden or backyard; and streets
are often not safe for young children to play in alone.

Third, a child needs to develop inside his brain a 'model of the world'. For this he needs a memory as described in Chapter 7, to store experience. He then uses his memory or model of the world to compare what is happening now with past experience of similar situations and then to make a decision — to act, to speak. All of us have a past, however meagre, and a memory to store it in. The experience which is stored comes from everything a child experiences.

Fourth, a child needs love and security; someone has to be 'mad about him'. Sometimes by middle class standards some poor families seem to live a harsh even cruel regime, but many with great effort do provide a caring home and good models. Here is one example:

> Their particular style of communication and the crudeness of their language make them appear less attractive than they really are. When Cruz screams at her three year old daughter, 'I'll pull your lungs out of your mouth!' and the child continues to disobey without apparent fear, it suggests that perhaps the child is quite secure in her mother's love . . . and if the children's hurts go unattended, it is equally true that in the long run their mother's lack of concern is not entirely inappropriate in an environment where toughness is necessary for survival. Soledad, may seem like a harsh, cruel, inconsistent mother by middle class standards, but one should also note how much time, energy and attention she gives to her children and how hard she tries to live up to her own ideal of a good mother. With much effort she has managed to provide them with a home, food and clothing, even with toys. She has not abandoned them, nor permitted anyone to abuse them, and she is devoted to them when they are ill (see Ginsburg, H. op.cit.).

But all this is needed for even minimal development of the brain. Millions of children live below their potential, though childhood should contain golden years of joy and opportunity. To maximize development the individuality of the child needs to be recognized and success found for each and every one. A good environment for play (including language) is a necessity, so that the model of the world built up by experience can be used to think well and to feel with sensitivity.

The role of the family in child rearing

A secure family life is necessary, with a definite leader. Family life may have its ups and downs, as we all know and although the mother has most contact with and influence on the children, the father's position is central. In a way he is like the sun. If he shines warmly it gives a glow to the family. If he is overcast with bad moods or shorttempered after a bad day at work, then this reflects on the family and there is tension, anxiety and rows. And with regard to educational attainment it has been shown that in families where both parents regularly talk to teachers about a child's progress, children are up to seven months ahead in reading and maths scores over those where only mothers were involved. Temporary father absence is associated with a decline in children's school attainment. Fathers need also to be actively involved with children. Low achievers at school and those most likely to be bored, are least likely to be taken on outings by father.[81]

A normal family with its brothers and sisters and ordinary warmhearted, fallible parents serves as a secure base from which a child can explore and test out his environment. It sets a standard for the child of what is right or wrong and what is accepted or refused, so that he can establish his own standards. The need for clear-cut and appropriate rules for children in the family is therefore crucial. They should know what the rules are, that they are fair, what will happen if the rules are broken and most important that rules change to fit the age and maturity of each individual child.

A family also helps a child to learn to share, to accept less of something so that others may have a share: and so the ideas of justice begin to take root. The parent-child 'system' allows a child to grow and develop well because the child has no way himself of releasing his potential whereas the parent-child unit, acting like a catalyst, does possess this capability, at least in his early years. When the child is older and at school the parent is no longer the principal teacher, but acts rather as a supporter of the school (and this implies real partnership). Nevertheless the parent continues to be the major figure responsible for the child's development as a person. The most valuable gifts a parent can give a child are time, fairly distributed between children and ungrudgingly given; also understanding, affection, respect, security, protection and moral strength while they are growing up. Also, it is important for a child to belong to a family where conversation among its members is abundant, straightforward and honest. The disappearance of the family meal is a retrograde step in this regard.

A child, as Jerome Kagan writes, credits his parents with extraordinary widsom (see *The Growth of the Child*). If they behave as if he is valuable, he takes these actions as evidence of his essential goodness. On the other hand, if they behave as if he is without worth, he begins to wonder about his capacity to be valued by someone else. Most important, a family helps to pick up the bits in times of stress and distress. Children remain dependent in some way on parents until long after they have left home, unless they choose to cut themselves off.

In a general sense the family has changed in the last two or three generations. It is now smaller, more prosperous and perhaps does not have the fun, the rough and tumble and the necessary sharing out, of the bigger families of the past. Often both parents work and share more equally the traditional role of the mother in bringing up children. The natural source of mothering-information, help, wise advice and a ready ear to a young mother — the grandma and other older female relations and friends and long established neighbours — is not always nearby, for families are more mobile and alone (one third of families move house every five years). Consequently children do not appreciate the pattern of generations as they did. Children (compared with 50 years ago) seldom meet death and it is avoided as a subject. And these days there are vast numbers of one-parent families. Although the family has changed in pattern its role in child rearing is still as crucial as ever it was. It is as the Court Report says:

> a social arrangement for the protection and rearing of children; a commitment by men and women, together or alone, to care as well as they can and for as along as is needed for the children born to them or chosen by adoption ... Although child-rearing patterns are changing and may change further the pattern we have described is still the central one in our society.

Chapter 13

Growth Patterns of the Middle Years

During this middle year period of growth big changes take place in children — in body size, in physiology and in social behaviour.[82] At the age of seven boys and girls in a top infant class are much the same in build, though boys are a shade taller, less plump and more muscular. By contrast at 12 most boys are only on the threshold of puberty but many girls are in the middle of it as judged by their growth spurts. These statements are of course about averages and need qualification. A boy reaches the great spurt of growth (one characteristic of puberty) at about 14 but it can take place between 9 and 15. Girls grow fastest at about 12 but the spurt can happen at any age between 10 and 15. Girls are much more advanced sexually than boys at 12 and, from about $10^1/_2$ to around 13, on average a shade taller, rather more muscular and heavier than boys. This does not mean of course that all girls are bigger than all boys at 12. There is a range but it is true that the tallest girls are appreciably taller than the biggest boys while the shortest girls are taller than the smallest boys.

In a class of 12 year olds in a middle or secondary school, therefore, the sex differences have opened up and there is a big variation in body size, strength, shape, degree of sexual maturity and in behaviour. These variations may be hard for the individual pupil to cope with and it is important for the teacher to understand these differences.

Details of body composition

This is a rather bare description of physical development, and some detail can be illuminating. From the age of seven in girls there is a gradual increase in body fat which continues through puberty. In boys there is an interesting pre-adolescent spurt in fat growth at about ten and then a loss of fat from limbs during puberty. But the gap in total body fat between girls and boys is considerable and persists, girls continuing to put on fat as adolescence proceeds while in boys the gain stops and reverses. The proportion of muscle tissue remains more constant in both sexes, contributing more weight in boys than in girls at all ages. One set of data (see Faulkner, F. and Tanner, J.M. op.cit.) gives the percentage of fat in girls of nine as around 16 per cent and in boys, 12 per cent; for muscle, the figures are, for girls 42 per cent, for boys 46 per cent. At 12 girls are about 22 per cent fat and 44 per cent muscle while boys are 18 per cent and 46 per cent respectively. At 15 girls still have around a fifth of their body weight as fat and this proportion continues at least in the young adult. Boys have shed some fat by about 15 and are down to about 15 per cent body weight. The proportion then drops to about 10 per cent in young adults. The puppy fat about which some girls are often embarrassed in adolescence gives them feminine curves and even at twelve increases their sexual attractiveness before they are mature enough to be interested in the opposite sex. This may be a contributing cause of anorexia nervosa which is considered in Chapter 16.

Apparently these broad trends in body composition mask a cyclical accumulation of fat and muscle during childhood but as stated, fat accumulation predominates in early childhood and puberty. In many children the rate of accumulation is greater than it should be and they become obese. Indeed obesity is a common condition with an incidence of at least 6 per cent in the early and middle school years; it may approach 20-30 per cent in adolescence, especially in girls, and is often accompanied by emotional and physical disability. Such children are often teased at home but more at school. They may become isolated because they are morose and difficult as well as physically sluggish. To be fat and happy, as C.G.D. Brook says, is not the lot of the fat child. Prevention of obesity is easier than cure. Treatment consists of a balanced diet containing fewer calories than the energy requirements of the child, supported accompanied by considerable psychotherapy.[83]

School tuck shops can be a pitfall for the obese and potentially obese. Too often they sell chocolate and biscuits easy to stock and undeniably popular, rather than fruit which can be stored for a limited period of time only.

Coordination

Regarding the coordination and physical capabilities of children in these years there appears to be little difference in strength, agility and balance between boys and girls before adolescence. Arm thrust and pull is similar, strength of leg muscles is no different but there is a marked difference in strength of hand grip, boys having the stronger grip from about nine or ten. This fact recalls the sex differences in forearm strength present from birth in boys and mentioned in Chapter 6. After the growth spurt boys catch up and overtake the girls and finish some 10 per cent greater in weight and most external measurements, and a good deal stronger.

Coordination of hand and eye improves steadily through the primary years. Children of five often have difficulty in catching or hitting a ball; at ten or eleven they are much more dexterous.

After adolescence too the coordination skills, strength and speed of boys increase. There is no shred of evidence that clumsiness is a characteristic of adolescence; a clumsy twelve or thirteen year old is likely to have been a clumsy eight year old and will grow up into a clumsy man or woman.

The Primary Survey (see *Primary Education in England*) makes it clear that, as children grow in physical strength and capabilities, team games are played with considerable enthusiasm and a great deal of skill is achieved by many. In addition, many schools encourage experience of body movement through dance, drama and large physical movements such as climbing, balancing and swimming. During the primary school years, the proportions of children change; legs become longer, bodies comparatively compact. The ability to run and leap increases from five to eleven. Children of ten and eleven outgrow the typical primary school hall and much of the apparatus provided in it. To cope with the growing powers of coordination and skill children of ten to thirteen need facilities that allow the development of football, cricket, hockey, netball and tennis. In these later years separation of boys and girls for some aspects of PE may be considered necessary. Boys' and girls' interests in games and athletics often run in different directions or, where they are similar, the greater speed and increasing strength of boys may indicate a need for separate teaching.

The importance of exercise

Perhaps something should be said at this point about the importance of regular exercise to the young and the need for parents to encourage individual, non-competitive sporting pleasures. The message is already getting across to adults that they may be able to stave off heart disease by preventive measures. There is understandably much less consciousness of the need for these measures among children but childhood is a vital time to start good behaviour patterns to prevent later disease.[84] Regular exercise helps to maintain a healthy weight and to keep blood pressure and cholesterol levels down. Children today do not walk much or take regular exercize in other forms. Besides the team games and physical education of school (which are unlikely to be continued when they leave) there is a need for parents to encourage walking and cycling for pleasure, also skating and perhaps, after twelve, golf, squash and tennis. The seeds sown in childhood may grow into pleasurable experiences later.

Girls and boys

Strength and toughness are important in the world of the small boy and advantage is given in this respect to the early maturer who at ten or eleven is likely to become top dog on the field, in the playground and in the street. At this age and in these circumstances, the small, immature boy is at a disadvantage. For most boys of eleven or twelve, however, the growth spurt and the manifestations of puberty are still to come. In girls on the other hand, the growth spurt starts at ten and reaches its maximum speed at twelve. The first sign of the changes of puberty in a girl is usually a slight growth of the central area of the breast — the 'bud'. This happens on average at about eleven and by twelve it has occurred in 75 per cent of girls. In more advanced girls the breasts may be fully mature by 12 but in others the process is not completed before 19.

Pubic hair growth appears in about half of girls at just over eleven, before the development of the breast bud and the adult distribution of hair in girls is usually attained between twelve and seventeen. In most boys, however, full adult hair is seldom reached until the mid-twenties. Hair first appears just after twelve but does not grow rapidly until the growth spurt at about fourteen.

Although the growth spurt happens earlier in girls than boys by about two years, other aspects of sexual development do not take place much later in boys than girls. Boys' reproductive organs start to develop about the same time as breasts in girls and complete sexual maturity is reached about the same average age in both sexes. Girls' looks at puberty — bigger than boys, with obvious breast development — make eleven and twelve year old boys look immature. But in boys the early development of the reproductive organs is concealed by clothes, and the obvious changes, the shooting up in height, deepening of the voice and the development of facial hair, do not happen until the reproductive organs are nearly mature.

Underlying the growth process and indeed the start of puberty is the control of hormones. No simple scheme is known for the hormonal control of growth in children but it is well understood that puberty is started by a nervous signal (about which nothing is known) from the hypothalamus at the base of the brain which triggers the pituitary gland into increasing the output of certain hormones. These in turn cause other hormones to be secreted in larger quantities from the ovaries or testes and adrenal glands and these hormones are the immediate causes of the changes of puberty — the growth spurt, changes in body fat/muscle and the appearance of the secondary sexual characteristics. In most girls the full spate of the hormone changes begins by twelve and in boys the activity of the adrenal glands is gradually increasing. As with the instruments of an orchestra, no hormone is more important than another in the process of growth and adolescence, and a deficiency of any will lead to impaired growth.

Developmental age

J.M. Tanner[34] has been a steady and convincing advocate of the importance of developmental rather than chronological age in education. The facts are that children who are physically mature for their age score slightly higher in intelligence tests than those who are less mature but of the same chronological age. The difference is consistent and detectable as early as six and a half. Early maturers have been found to be significantly more successful in 11+ tests than late maturers though as far as it is known the difference in intelligence tests scores between early and late maturers vanishes as each completes his or her growth. It should be emphasized however that the demonstration of these relationships in large groups of children does not imply that all large or early-maturing children are more intelligent than all small or late maturing ones. Similarly in emotional development, few top classes of primary schools are without children who have started their growth spurt with an increase in self-consciousness. In the 11-13 years of middle and secondary schools most girls are 'mature', most boys not. As Tanner points out 'when boys and girls are educated together we must never lose sight of the fact that girls are physically and emotionally more advanced at all ages than boys'.

In girls, the early developer, conscious of her developing breasts, may slouch and find the public conditions of showers after games or PE an agony that needs great understanding from adults. In relation to the clumsiness mentioned earlier, the girl who slouches and wears a shapeless cardigan to hide her growing breasts appears clumsy to the beholder. The late maturer may have his or her problems too, wondering privately whether he or she will ever grow up into a sexually normal adult. In these respects and others it is most important that teachers should discuss the normality of human variation at this time, to reassure the girl, for example, one of whose breasts enlarges before the other, or the boy who is embarrassed by the temporary enlargement of his breasts. Time will put these worries right but they are hard to bear at the time. Indeed if children are not taught about the wide variance in normal growth and development, they perceive such variance as abnormal, to the detriment in some cases of their psychological development.

Throughout this book the biological uniqueness of the individual has been stressed. Abilities and personalities differ from individual to individual and some children develop early and others late. All this is hard evidence for the importance of the notion of developmental age. However, for administrative purposes in education the convenient but very misleading criterion of chronological age has to be used: that is, the age from birth.

Developmental age is educationally a more sensible criterion because it is based on a flexible and dynamic and not an archaic, rigid view of growth and development. All would be straightforward if all children jumped their developmental hurdles at the same time, but the evidence tells us that they do not. Age of admission to school, age of transfer from one school to another, age of leaving, classification by IQ and examinations, the type of curriculum, are all mainly based on chronological age.

The basic aim of most schools is to develop the potentialities of the individual child, and to create the right sort of atmosphere in which he can learn and develop his abilities, both social and intellectual. Schools strive to do this and to 'know individuals' despite the differing rates of development of the children in their charge. The Newsom report,[85] a great educational report, makes this relevant point about human individuality:

> There were well over two and three-quarter million boys and girls in maintained secondary schools in 1962, all of them individuals, all different. We must not lose sight of the differences in trying to discover what they have in common.

Chapter 14

Growth of the Mind in the Middle years

The last chapter emphasized that considerable physical changes happen in the middle years of schooling. A visitor to a middle school wrote that what struck him about it was that the absence of seven year olds and the presence of twelve (or thirteen) year olds 'shifts the school's centre of gravity. The school gets a cutting edge and robustness, almost a manly quality'.[86] It is certainly true that for the teacher of the oldest pupils the problems are numerous: social and emotional as well as of knowledge and subject expertise.

The growing powers of the mind

While evidence about what is happening inside the brain of a child during these middle years of growth is sparse, it is clear that, like the body, the mind is making great strides forward. Observations on school children between five and eleven demonstrate the growing ability to put things together so that the world is better understood. These children were asked to look at blocks of different shapes: triangles, squares and crosses. Each child was then asked to put his hand behind a screen and feel another block of the same or different shape and then say if they were the same or not. Further tests simply moved the child's hand through the outline of a given shape. The number of times the children scored correct answers was used as a measure of the ability to connect sight, feel and movement. There was a steady increase of score from the age of five to eleven. At the later age there were few mistakes but some five year olds were very skilful too.

Clearly there is some brain machinery developing which is concerned with making sense of one kind of sensation in terms of another and which goes on maturing up to about eleven and no doubt beyond. Presumably, as Chapter 9 pointed out, language development is similar. A child's ability to move on from the mere learning of words as they are specifically taught, to putting them into combinations never before said or heard and being understood, and himself understanding the same words again in new combinations, must mirror physical maturation of brain structures about which we as yet know very little. And as referred to in Chapter 10, drawing and painting can make children's thinking visible.

Concrete and formal thinking

Throughout this book the basic fact of human individuality of body and mind has been stressed. In this context the Plowden Report (1967) noted that individual differences between children of the same age are so great that any class, however homogeneous, must always be treated as a group of children who need individual and different attention; each needs a 'special' environment such as a different reading scheme, a different stress on the use of apparatus and concrete material for mathematics, a different shade of firmness and so on. Thus at the chronological age of eleven, some children in terms of mental growth are at the concrete operational stage of Piaget, mentioned in Chapter 10; others will be at the threshold of the stage of 'formal operational thinking' which is considered in more detail in Chapter 15; a few will be well into this latter stage. Briefly, the formal stage is so called because the subject matter which a child can deal with can be *ideas* and events outside previous experience; its hallmark is the ability to reason logically. The concrete operational thinker, who Piaget suggests is mainly found in the age range 7-11 years, is still concerned with ordering, classifying, rearranging *things,* even if he does this in his head.

Such a cut and dried account, as every teacher will know, bears little relationship to the reality before him in his class or indeed within his own experience of himself. Jeanette Coltham[87] expressed the point well, that such is the flexibility of the mind in its functioning that adults and children will use at one time primitive methods of thinking and at others those of a higher order. She also gives a clear warning of the possible difficulties of a break at eleven without proper continuity not only between schools but even between classes in the same school:

It is worth remembering that, however adult we consider our

powers of thought, we do at times use a concrete (or even earlier) level of thinking, and particularly when we encounter a novel situation, an unfamiliar problem or an aspect of knowledge which we have not previously studied. In order to reach a higher level and to grasp the necessary concepts, we particularize and help ourselves by using actual examples before trying to generalise or attain an abstract idea. But we have already become quite proficient at the formal level and know that we can regain it. For those who are still at the transitional stage, there is no such certainty and progress could undoubtedly be slowed down if this stage, together with the natural dislocation brought by transfer from a comfortable and known to an excitingly (or frighteningly) different environment, is not recognised and catered for in secondary schools.

Primary to secondary school

Just as Chapter 10 remarked on the fact that starting school at five is a major event in the life of a child, so for many children the change from primary to secondary school, to a 'frighteningly different' environment can be traumatic for an eleven year old. The smallest secondary school looks vast and complex, the big boys tower. The search for specialist rooms set in large blocks of buildings along unfamiliar corridors can bring to some children the fear of being lost. Specialist teaching while having its own beneficial stimulus, will bring a child into contact with many more teachers than in his primary school. Most secondary schools ease this transition by links with feeder primary schools which allow the child to visit the school for a day or half a day to meet his form teacher and see the school. Some secondary schools also try to group children in forms which contain some children from the same primary school. A sound knowledge of the individual child is crucial. As one Head[88] wrote:

> The child who arrives at school is not a clean slate upon which we are free to make our mark. Each child comes from a particular environment involving multiple factors which are contributing to his development as an individual.

It is recorded in *Primary Education in England* that about half the primary schools receive information on the subsequent progress of their children at their new schools. On the issue of curricular continuity, however, *Primary Education in England* emphasises that much needs to be done: 'the importance of continuity in the curriculum of the schools was largely overlooked ... this can be achieved only if there is regular and systematic consultation between teachers from the associated schools'. Similarly, more could be done to ease transition between classes within a school, primary or middle, by the use of individual folders of a child's work.

What schools do to develop thinking

To return to the process of mental growth: *Primary Education in England* gives examples of how teachers provide opportunities (though not enough) for older primary school children to follow a line of argument, to evaluate evidence and alternative points of view or to arrive at judgements through discussion and in their own writing. Many of the activities described will clearly involve thinking at the concrete stage, for it is likely that the main mental development during adolescence is in concrete operational thinking and only about the top 20 per cent will have achieved early formal thinking by the age of thirteen or fourteen.

As the Primary Report points out, whether children are working at first hand or with secondary sources, they will need help in noticing relevant features and in generalizing from their observations.

> Specially devised activities to support practice in classifying and generalising, for example, exercises involving the manipulation of coloured shapes, may have a useful place but they are a poor substitute for the varied and interesting work with plants, animals and all kinds of natural and man-made materials and objects through which these cognitive skills are, in a minority of schools, developed in various parts of the curriculum.

The cognitive skills referred to will, as indicated earlier, be mainly at the concrete operational stage of thinking but a good teacher will be providing this kind of experience to prepare the minds of some of his pupils to tackle a problem in a more mature systematic way by considering a range of possibilities and eliminating all but the most feasible, as the example from the Primary Report given below shows. The type of thinking encouraged in this example is a mark of the formal operational thinker. Similarly if a child of thirteen can make a stab at such a question in his science lessons as 'why are penguins larger as they get nearer the South Pole' and thereby use his knowledge of surface area to volume ratio, he is moving towards the formal operational stage of thinking!

Perhaps the children who lose out in these middle years are the more able who will gain a great deal by delving deeper into mathematics, by inquiry and experiment in science, by being introduced to books of travel and biography. It is these children in particular who need more of the kind of activity described in *Primary Education in England*.

The top junior age children referrred to above were mapping the course of a river near the school.

> The children followed a small tributary which disappeared underground and the teacher asked the children to think about where it might have gone. This led to a careful examination of the surrounding area and the contours of the land. The children produced a number of possible alternatives and subsequently put forward arguments suggesting which was the most likely course, with some pupils producing evidence to support their different points of view. While the course of the tributary was not finally discovered, the children had valuable experience in presenting their cases and marshalling evidence to support them.

Developing social and moral learning

Besides a growing capacity to think at different levels there is also a growth in social and moral learning. At first, rules need to be imposed by home and school and of course a few need to persist. As a child grows up through these middle years he comes to understand the basis of restraints of one kind or another and accepts them. It is in this way that he gradually learns a measure of tolerance, to make allowances, and to share, to find out where he stands with his family and friends and what he can expect of them and what they can ask of him. In the development of these attitudes most schools teach children to respect their surroundings and take care of books and other materials and equipment. Cooperative work in Art and Craft, in drama and much else provides abundant opportunities for teaching how and why to behave in a responsible and considerate way. And, very important, both home and school will teach about choice between doing or saying this or that. The ability to choose between alternatives requires the ability to reason, a capacity which lies at the heart of morality. Schools in the middle years have developed 'choice programmes' so that children learn to choose and say why they have made such a choice. Choices are of course within narrow limits. They may be between a variety of media in which to express what they have thought or imagined, or between books they want to read. They are thus developing 'normal autonomy' by exercizing a measure of responsible choice.

These are the years where good, steady friendships develop with football, making dens, building models, watching television serials as part of weekly activities. In these years, too, parents share a good deal in the children's interests and enthusiasm and can give companionship as well as opening the mind to new experiences. They are mostly good easy years for parents who fly kites, cycle, fish in the canal, go to matches and walk together with their children.

Chapter 12 refers to the crucial importance of the family as a source of security and the place where children should be able to relax, talk, read, play, argue, pursue their hobbies and so on. Many families now do not give children this security and their emotional development during these years may be impeded by an inadequate 'self-image'. Some regard themselves as failures and the gap in achievement between these and those children who enjoy school and a happy home-life widens. Some children are certainly under-estimated by their teachers and do not gain as much as they should from their schooling.

Chapter 15

A General View of Adolescence

Parents and teachers are well aware that the large majority of young people pass through what can be a period of turmoil and inner worry during adolescence yet come to experience pleasure and stability in their personal lives.

One might wonder why adolescence should be such a turbulent time and why much of the adolescent's behaviour, both as an individual and in groups, is confusing. It is no new phenomenon. Shakespeare in *The Winter's Tale* struck a modern note:

> I would there were no age between ten and three-and-twenty, or that youth would sleep out the rest; for there is nothing in the between but getting wenches with child, wronging the ancientry, stealing, fighting.

The search for identity

Physical and intellectual growth are rapid during adolescence and together with hormonal changes may be hard to cope with. For one thing, intellectual, emotional and social development tend to lag behind sexual development. Then pressures in school life can intensify the confusion: 'transfer at 11+, the search for personal identity ('Who am I') and the need for close relationships, the crisis of examinations and the search for a vocational role' as one head put it (see *Truancy and Behavioural Problems in Some Urban Schools*). To add to all this, many adolescents, perhaps most, feel inadequate at times and wonder whether they are attractive or tough or healthy or bright enough. Some may feel a failure because they do not match up to a personal ideal. Some feel confused and lonely. Others are worried and uncertain about their behaviour to their parents, for example, or their private thoughts. Some feel guilty about nasty arguments with those they love. Many are rebellious but rebellion is healthy in the young while timidity is not. It was Oscar Wilde who wrote 'children begin by loving their parents; after a time they judge them; rarely, if ever, do they forgive them'. Now is the time of the second stage!

Adolescents are bursting with energy and excitement and show a desire to rush out to experiment and live. All this is perfectly natural because active exploration in many directions is necessary before making long-term commitments. But the desire to do this or that has a brake put on it by authority and often by lack of money. In the midst of all these changes and confusions, an adolescent's image of himself is changing and he may wonder what part of him is his real self. This feeling of confusion persists in most people but in adolescence it is at its peak. The authority figures are chiefly parents and teachers and it is the former who usually bear the brunt of anger which is often expressed in words, rebellion and moodiness. Hidden flaws in family relationships are likely to become more evident in adolescence because he or she is having to cope with growing up while parents have their own mid-life difficulties to sort out. Two points made by Dr Stewart Prince[89] are important in understanding some of the problems of an adolescent. One is parental envy of a teenager, the other is the pattern of his or her first few years of life:

In our day, parents frequently seem to envy their teenagers their increased educational opportunities, their gear, their relative freedom, and, of course, most understandably, their youth. At the social level I believe it is this envy which accounts for the odium with which young people are so unjustly regarded and treated.

A second generalisation is that the breakdown which brings the adolescent to a psychiatric clinic can only be understood by careful study of his development in the first few years of life. Flaws in this early development often announce themselves by transient symptoms and it is common for the child to be able to cope with his difficulties and develop apparently normally through the junior school years.

When he moves into the turbulent period of puberty the stress often breaks down his defences and so he presents at the clinic with depression, fear of school, behaviour disorder, or a myriad of other symptom complexes.

Most adolescents want to go with the crowd often to gain support after family rows about their ideals and feelings and perhaps to avoid the growing necessity at seventeen or eighteen of being an individual, lonely and responsible. The adolescent in particular fears failure in a social situation (and in many of us this fear remains) for he imagines that people are more critical than they are; because of this he may make an excuse to get out of a social commitment rather than chance failure. If parents are emotionally mature and supportive and willing to listen to a point of view with humility and a sense of humour, this greatly affects a boy or girl's behaviour for the better. The vast majority of adolescents, though often rude and disobedient and appearing at times openly to despise the values of their parents, love and need them; they need security and fair rules yet want to rebel against them.

One might ask why adolescent behaviour is like this. Perhaps it is an evolutionary anachronism left over from when it was necessary for boys to learn to survive into manhood. Meanwhile adults want to creep away and ignore the excesses without trying to understand how the once vital energy and enthusiasm to survive could be used to good purpose.

Many adolescents have great difficulty in adapting to their rapid physical growth and the complex bodily changes of puberty. They are often ill at ease with their bodies and tend to be hypersensitive to minor physical disadvantages. It is striking how often the child with some physical disability will seem to tolerate this without difficulty until coming into adolescence, when it becomes a source of great distress.

If a young person, feels his body is abnormal, or has acne, or is painfully shy or has BO or stammers, he is more likely to avoid his peers in adolescence and to avoid situations where he can be compared. He will be more inclined to isolate himself so that by the time he is seventeen or eighteen his view of himself as being different and perhaps abnormal is not easily rectified.

Moses Laufer[90] illustrates this last important point with a physical analogy. If a child breaks his leg and the leg is not properly set, the bone may heal but the child will limp. This in turn may affect his ability to play sports, to have friends and to do what other people do. If the broken leg had been set correctly, the result would have been different. Sympathy, understanding and practical help from parents, teachers and others are necessary to help a boy or girl through a bad patch.

Since adolescence is one of the most formative periods of the entire life-span, comparable to the early years already described the environment of childhood and adolescence needs to provide reasonable support, guidance and models of suitable behaviour from parents and teachers. School activities too can help the adolescent to use his developing capacities not only in sport, outdoor pursuits and through lessons but in teaching him to recognize and respect the individual, and, with parents, help him towards a good sense of values and moral qualities: honesty, integrity, the need to cooperate, to take responsibility and the need to do a fair day's work for a fair day's pay. At the same time school provides time for adolescents to share problems with their peers and obtain support from them as they develop normally through school. This support from family, peers and school is important, for the development of the mind is a continuum and one stage prepares for the next.

Stages of thought

A few bright children of thirteen or fourteen can reason logically, starting with premises and drawing the conclusions which follow. It is the thinking of the intelligent, rational adult, though not combined with the judgement that comes through experience, rather, thinking of unclouded directness. It is called 'formal' because as stated earlier, *ideas* can now be manipulated and Piaget holds that it is approximately reached by about twelve. Children of nine or ten cannot do this so easily because the content of their thinking is limited, as Chapter 14 suggested, to previous or direct concrete experience. If a child of eight is asked the question, Edith is fairer than Susan, Edith is darker than Lily: who is darkest? most cannot solve it in their heads. Yet if they were asked to arrange three dolls in serial order the task would be easy for them.

Not only is the ability to reason involved in formal thinking but the capacity to make testable hypotheses from data, to set a fact in a general setting, to use models to explain phenomena and relate one observation to another quite different one: in other words, to see patterns. For example, to begin to understand the subtleties of the balance of nature in an oakwood and to predict what might happen to the balance if one animal or plant species died out. Or to use the model of natural selection to explain a fact: the camouflage and behaviour of a stick insect which allows it to survive and breed. This is, of course, describing the kind of intellectual activity associated with many subjects — mathematics, science and history as three examples. Much of the experimental science taught in the secondary school from eleven assumes that a bright thirteen or fourteen year old can make tentative hypotheses, arrived at on the basis of preliminary inquiries, and discuss and design experiments or make observations to test a hypothesis.

It was held by Piaget that once a child can think like this, then he can apply such a method of analysis to any problem, regardless of the content. Experience of the classroom however, reveals a complex situation: that 'formal' thinking may take place in one subject and primitive 'concrete' thinking to solve problems of equal complexity in another. Probably the great majority of thirteen or fourteen year olds are still developing in the concrete operational stage of thought and indeed most of us conduct our day-to-day affairs using concrete thinking only.

Aspects of Secondary Education in England indicates the level of expectation about the stage of a child's mind at 14-16 and assumes in some of the criteria (3 and 4 below) used in the survey, a formal stage of thinking. Thus HMI engaged in the survey, inspected the work in science with certain criteria in mind. Four of them are given below.

1. Is the pupil observant? That is to say, does he see all that there is to see or does he rely on being told what to see?
2. Does he select from his observations those which have a bearing on the problem before him?
3. Does he look for patterns in what he observes and is he able to tie in to his current observations others he has made earlier? That is to say, can he recall other observations which contribute to the pattern?
4. Does he seek to explain the patterns? If he can offer more than one explanation, does he attempt to rank them in order of plausibility?

A few children arrive at this level of thinking quite early, at eleven or twelve, most much later, and some may never reach it. Pradip, an Indian boy, aged thirteen described in the DES pamphlet on Gifted Children[91] was articulate and clear-minded, and explained lucidly the snags in arguing about the natural distribution of woodlice from an experiment with many variables in it (light, shade, dry and damp) he had set up in the laboratory. He saw, too, without prompting, that his laboratory experiments needed to be checked by observation of the animals in natural conditions. Pradip was into the early formal stage of thought.

Unlike Pradip, most children at thirteen or fourteen are unable to hold a problem in the mind to analyse it, to cope with much beyond two variables (if the pressure of a gas is raised then its volume will drop. But does a drop in volume necessarily mean that the pressure has gone up? Not if a third variable is involved — temperature) or look for patterns in what they observe, or to apply facts already learned to a new situation. Sometimes children seem to have mastered a principle because they can, without real understanding, follow it through. But there is often a gap between the 'outward façade' and 'inward organization' as Piaget pointed out. Once a gap is left it may never be filled and so the foundations of a subject remain shaky. Understanding through doing is crucial for most children and is the basis of new learning, while understanding by explaining it to another is important too. The business of thinking aloud helps to expose gaps and weaknesses in understanding.

Most adolescents of thirteen or fourteen still have some of the curiosity of younger children, though now, and especially at 14+, it is tempered with a strong streak of utilitarianism.

Adolescence is of course a time when young people become concerned with the world of work, exploring careers, looking for jobs and obtaining work experience. They are understandably utilitarian. A high rate of unemployment among the young not only has an economic impact but can seriously affect their mental health.

Education for unemployment is a fashionable topic for discussion. But such a curriculum (whatever it is), instead of preparing a young person to seek work, might take the edge off natural ambition and optimism. The crucial and rather obvious point is that sound teaching and a broad curriculum provide a good foundation for life whether times are lean or plentiful.

Reflectiveness

Though young people are often utilitarian, they have another side which is idealistic and thoughtful. Perhaps one of the marks of adolescence which goes hand in hand with the developing power to reason is 'reflectiveness' — a capacity that does not always go with the ability to achieve high examination grades. In Chapter 14 it was suggested that the ability to make choices lies at the heart of morality. The quality of such reflective thought depends of course on training judgement to become pertinent and discriminating. Most areas of the curriculum help to develop judgement: art, literature, science, religious education, to name some. But within these curricular areas those topics that enhance 'thoughtfulness' about oneself and others are often concerned with race, politics, sex or religion and may well deal with crucial areas of choice such as abortion, spare-part surgery, euthanasia, atomic power, pollution, poverty and so on. The fifteen and sixteen year old is very ready to have a view on issues which are concerned with the outside world and in the process his moral autonomy is strengthened.

Less academic children

Earlier in this chapter, reference was made to gifted children, but a proportion of young people at this stage of development are not strong academically. Some of the very slowest of them are not well provided for, as both the recent *Aspects of Secondary Education* and *Slow Learners in Secondary Schools*[78] show. Their learning difficulties, which are complex, will not be described here but those inherent in a feckless home and in genetic endowment bear heavily on some while others have disabilities which need a measure of special care. These children above all need the concrete experience arising, for instance, from a study of the local environment, opportunities for observation and experiment and, most important, the chance to talk about and record however simply what they have seen, felt and understood. Too many seem to be exposed to a curriculum which is a ramshackle continuation of disconnected subject teaching. *Aspects of Secondary Education* says this about their provision:

> They frequently had the advantage of being taught in smaller classes, with the possibility of receiving greater individual attention, but the programmes offered to them were seldom successfully pitched at a level which both retained interest and demanded worthwhile achievement. Schools made various attempts to cater for needs as they perceived them. Sometimes a considerable choice of practical activities was offered, but with little coherence in the curriculum as a whole. In other schools 'packaged courses' might be designed to give greater coherence, with large blocks of time devoted to some form of combined studies, but the content of such work was often observed to be undemanding, and the rest of the pupil's programme outside the special course could be even more inconsequential.

Others who are academically in the rung *above* the slowest but may share some of their characteristics leave school at the earliest opportunity, some only eighteen months short of their majority, physically mature and not at all anxious to extend their education.

The girls have often been going steady with a boy from thirteen onwards and look forward to marriage at sixteen or seventeen regarding work as a stop-gap between school and marriage. If, as indicated above, they are offered watered down academic courses which make them feel less and less adequate as they grow older — a feeling constantly sharpened by the examination successes of their academically brighter peers — then problems of disruption are likely to arise.

Many of these pupils will have poor vocabulary, a short concentration span and an inability to see 'connections' or to follow simple instructions, and it is such skills which should have priority over knowledge. Many boys and girls have difficulty with reading, writing and mathematics but are not in the main 'unintelligent' and may perform below their true capacity. Because of a disadvantaged background they may start school at five with an IQ score some 20 points below that of their peers who have had the advantage of stories on mother's knee, personal conversation with adults, books and other stimuli as well as peace and quiet. They very often have difficulty in realising the significance of what they have been asked to learn. They are often antagonistic to school and school authority so that their attendance record is poor. Apathy and indifference can mark them out.

To take a more cheerful view, however, those who possess some or all of the above characteristics have often demonstrated their potential in some other way.

They are often able to cope with a very difficult environment. Indeed a boy who is capable of surviving in a slum environment or on a bleak housing estate must have considerable adaptability. He is often able to concentrate for long periods of time when he is working at things of interest to him — the complexities of car engines. He can show considerable insight into human behaviour and can often show more maturity and ability to function in various social situations, for example camp, than many academic young people. Usually he is able to talk about something meaningful to him with enthusiasm and interest even though he can not write much about it.

Remarkably, after leaving school, some of these boys and girls learn to master complex skills in industry, commerce and building. Some become buyers and sellers in the retail trade. Even some so-called 'failures' manage to pass severe driving tests to become drivers of heavy goods vehicles and to obtain PSV licences. Experienced heads say candidly that they have sometimes been wrong and have been surprised by how well some boys and girls have done. It is quite clear (and evidence given earlier about the plasticity and resilience of the brain confirms it) that some of these duller young people — are late maturers and have the capacity to mature well on into their mid-twenties, thirties and forties: all is not lost by eighteen or nineteen!

Realistically, however, many will still find themselves in dead-end jobs and unemployed and these are the pupils (perhaps up to 20 per cent of a school's intake in some cases) for whom the job of finding a worthwhile curriculum is very difficult. As Sir Alec Clegg said, they above all lack that most powerful of all educational forces — parental aspiration — and often do not have what HMI described a century ago as 'that recognition which our natures crave for and acknowledge with a renewed endeavour'.[92] In 1979 HMI (see *Aspects of Secondary Education in England*) added to this truth, this harder but equally true observation about the needs of these pupils:

> The causes may not lie exclusively within the schools, but perhaps schools need to consider whether comparisons with their abler contemporaries may have led to unduly low expectations of these pupils by their teachers or by the pupils themselves. It is perhaps also too readily assumed that uniform teaching methods are suitable, whereas greater flexibility and variety in teaching approaches may be needed.

Chapter 16

Some Special Problems of Adolescence

Nutrition

The importance of a good diet during periods of rapid growth and development has been well known for some time. Previous chapters have considered the links between good nutrition and the physical health of the child. The improvements in health of children over the past century are largely due to a better diet,[93] improved hygiene and the control of infection. The nutritional problems of adolescence, another period of rapid growth and development, have been surprisingly neglected. There has been a tendency to treat adolescents as adults in their dietary needs, and the Ministry of Food during the 1939-45 war took much persuading to obtain extra rations for them. Even now, surprisingly little is known about their precise needs. The WHO report on *Problems of Children of School Age (14-18)*[94] states that the basic nutritional requirements of adolescents have yet to be clearly established though they must be different from either children or adults because of the growth spurt, sexual development, increased physical exercise, metabolic rates and emotional stress. V.H. Mottram[95] recommends plenty of milk and cheese as well as high calorie foods, as growth is very rapid and bones are being calcified. Girls should be encouraged to take as much as or more than boys of iron-containing foods, green vegetables, eggs and liver. If there is reluctance they can be recommended as good for the complexion!

Industrialization and social change have created new nutritional problems which affect both children and adolescents, such as the disappearance of the family meal, and pre-processed and canteen food. All these together with food faddisms (suddenly becoming a vegetarian) snacks and soft drinks are very relevant to the diet of an adolescent who often eschews the pudding, meat and two vegetables of a traditional home. Nevertheless the nutritional values of convenience foods are in many cases unknown and in some cases may prove to be of equal or even better value than more traditional foods.

Extremes of overweight and underweight are important issues in adolescence. Not all obese children eat excessively; they may need very few calories. It is not known whether obese children and adolescents are inactive because they are obese, or obese because they are inactive, but there is no doubt that increased physical activity plays a part in the prevention and treatment of obesity. Most of these children and adolescents have emotional problems. Perhaps obesity may be reasonably prevented in younger school children by diet and exercise, but in adolescence a strong genetic component is likely to be operating, to which may be added the difficulties of parental control over adolescent eating habits. Exercise and control of food intake are necessary but the emotional problems that may be coupled with fatness are likely to be deep-rooted, and expert medical advice may be necessary.

Obesity is, of course, becoming a matter of concern in developed countries like our own, both because of its increasing prevalence and because of the growing recognition that its roots lie in early childhood and its consequences extend into adulthood and old age.

Underweight in teenagers may be due to different causes such as the rapid growth spurt, or, more commonly, self-imposed diets. In extreme cases those who undereat may suffer from anorexia nervosa, a condition which is on the increase and affects twelve times as many girls as boys. Its causes remain an enigma to many of the doctors who treat it. Indeed at the beginning of the twentieth century, published work disclosed and undisguised hostility towards young fasting girls.[96] In 1911 Albutt and Rolleston described anorexia nervosa under the heading of hysteria in the following way:

> out of such material, when the friends and surroundings supply the element of fraud and credulity, are made the fasting girls who from time to time become notorious and whose exploits have been known to terminate in death.

Sometimes anorexia is triggered off when the girl decides that she is too fat, perhaps after seeing a recent photograph of herself or following teasing about ordinary adolescent plumpness by family and friends. The sudden feeling of being too fat and the determination to diet often cloaks a deeper sense of inadequacy of which she is unaware. Sometimes she blames her fatness for all her difficulties, which might be an inability to live up to her own and other people's expectations of her, or her relationships with friends, family and boyfriends. Sometimes, perhaps unconsciously, she wishes to avoid adult sexuality by shedding the roundness that makes her attractive. Often these anorexic girls, unlike many adolescents who are normally rebellious, do not give their parents or teachers much trouble in respect of drugs, alcohol, late-night parties and boyfriends. They do not seem to want to establish their independence by challenging authority. Physically, a girl feels fat even though she is not and if asked to draw herself portrays an obese person because she has a distorted body image. A boy is more likely to be more accurate in his judgements. Perhaps anorexia in a girl arises both from her dieting behaviour and from family stresses and strains. The rarity of it in boys may be relevant to their indifference to their size and shape or else, more probably, their wish to be big and strong.

Motorcycles

Accidental injury is the commonest cause of death among adolescents. The motorcycle, scooter, moped and old 'banger', of doubtful safety, are in part responsible for the heavy toll of death among older adolescents. Add to the possession of a motorbike (the most lethal of vehicles) the thrill of speed and rush of air in the face, the smell of the exhaust, all the trappings — pennants, badges, stickers, leather jackets, decorated helmets — and the adolescent's desire for excitement and speed, his lack of caution, the ever increasing volume of traffic on the roads, and there is a formula for death and serious injury. The statistics for fatal and serious casualties among 17-19 year old riders of two-wheeled motor vehicles in Great Britain in 1971 was 4,700; in 1977 this had risen to 8,600 (see *Social Trends*). No one would wish to curb a spirit of adventure in an adolescent boy and the police in many areas have formed a splendid liaison service with schools which helps the adolescent in a practical way towards safety in riding his bike. They stress the importance of possessing a good helmet and avoiding cheap (and dangerous) ones; the need for a clean unscratched vizor to prevent dazzle in the rider. But as the Court Report stated, the figures for road traffic accidents of all kinds involving the young are too high for complacency and although much work has been done, further preventive measures need to be planned, executed and evaluated with urgency, either by voluntary or statutory bodies.

Sexual maturation

The lowering of the age of puberty is accompanied by an increase in promiscuous sexual behaviour among adolescents and there has been growing concern about the numbers of pregnancies occurring in young girls, particularly in those under sixteen (see *Fit for the Future*). In 1977, 3,625 or 1 in 500 girls under 16 became pregnant. Out of every 100 pregnancies to under 16 year olds approximately 63 were legally terminated, 36 resulted in a live birth and one in a stillbirth. In 1977, 8,424 or 1 in 44 single girls aged 16 became pregnant. Out of every 100 pregnancies to single 16 year olds, approximately 49 were legally terminated, 34 were born alive to unmarried girls and 17 to mothers who married before the birth. Less than 1 in 100 resulted in a stillbirth.[97] As the Court Report observed, often the saddest part of this picture is the children who are having children. Each is a matter of grave concern, a tragedy for the girl, her parents and the baby. Added to the personal tragedy is the loss and disruption of schooling. And these school girls who become pregnant are not abnormal: the bulk are popular with their fellow pupils. The Preface to *Pregnant at School* underlines what has just been quoted from the Court Report:

> the quality and compassion of social policy in England may be more easily tested and discerned in the little universe where most pregnant school girls must experience fear, the disruption of relationships and expectations and a premature shouldering of adult responsibilities, which puts an end to the freedom and gaiety belonging to youth, than in the major areas of high policy.

Michael Schofield[98], fifteen years ago, found that 14 per cent of boys and 2 per cent of girls had experienced sexual intercourse by sixteen, the percentages rising to 34 per cent and 17 per cent by the age of eighteen when marriage was becoming common. These statistics (though somewhat old) hardly show the extinction of virginity which was then gloomily forecast by some and bear out the natural modesty of these shy awkward years. Christine Farrell's[99] more recent statistics showed that 12 per cent of the girls in her sample had had sexual intercourse before the age of sixteen, and though 12 per cent is a smaller proportion than commonly thought, it is a substantial number.

One of the most worrying statistics in Schofield's report was that 84 per cent of boys and 82 per cent of girls had some knowledge of birth control but 'the majority neither took precautions themselves nor insisted on their partners using any'. More recently, Christine Farrell (Farrell, C. op. cit.) found that less than half of the 1,500 young people in her sample of 16-19 year olds had received information on birth control in their early teens. It seems likely therefore that substantial numbers of young people are sexually active for several years before seeking advice on contraception. The reasons for them not doing so — whether ignorance, fear or deliberate choice — are unclear. Perhaps the avoidance of advice is a problem in Social Classes IV and V, but this is speculative. Evidence from *Social Trends* shows the current use of contraceptives by the under-20s having intercourse as 60 per cent of women using the pill, 25 per cent some other form of contraceptive device and only 15 per cent using none. Is a high proportion of the latter in the lower social classes?

Schofield also produced data on the inhibiting influences to sexual intercourse. An important restraint (fifteen years ago) in boys and girls was the fear of pregnancy but the most usual restraint for girls and an important one for boys was a moral one. This is not surprising because for generations, conscience, the unwanted baby, fear of God and the spirochaete have been firm allies in saving us from the flesh.

Pregnant adolescents increasingly resort to abortions, as indicated earlier, and the majority of pregnant girls are very vulnerable. As the Court Report states 'when abortion is under consideration, skilled counselling and the opportunity for discussion and advice should be made available before any decision is taken'. It might be added that even the safest abortion increases the chances of miscarriage in a subsequent pregnancy, by 10 per cent. And many abortion patients do not know that there is a risk of cervical damage in the case of a woman who has never had a baby before. Here the cervix is artificially dilated during pregnancy termination and a muscle is forced open that has never been used before, with a risk of damage and future problems.

Freer sexual activity among teenagers has been accompanied by an increase in sexually transmitted disease. The number of young people under twenty seen as new patients at hospital clinics in Great Britain in 1966 and treated for syphilis or gonorrhoea, was about 6,000, half men, half women. In 1977, 6,000 men and 8,000 women were seen (see *Social Trends*).

It is easy to moralize about the increase of VD but there may be other reasons for it besides the trend to early maturity and the emphasis on sex in advertising, films and popular reading. Ignorance about the transmission and detection of VD, a decline in religious faith, lack of discipline in home life and different codes of parental supervision in different families (which is one symptom of the disruption of family life) may all play their part.

Drink and drugs

Linked to the questions of teenage pregnancy and VD is the problem of drink, which, when taken in excess, relaxes self-restraint. Older teenagers use pubs often because there is nowhere else for them to meet and talk. Most pub-visiting is innocent and quite unconnected with even moderate amounts to drink. But some boys and girls of fifteen or sixteen look as old as eighteen, and with liberal pocket money, start to drink in pubs; perhaps this kind of drinking can lead, in a few, to alcoholism.

Parties in homes or clubs now seem to be quite different from those even ten years ago. Now there is often alcoholic drink available and not much food and some parents leave them to it. It is probably wise for parents to permit limited drinking at parties or gatherings of young people in the home or elsewhere. Indeed, John Davies and Barrie Stacey[100] in a survey, in *Teenagers and Alcohol,* approve of moderate drinking in the home:

> This may serve to provide a drinking model for the group and might reduce the chances of excessive drinking outside the home. The findings suggest that where parents forbid certain behaviours, including drinking, they in fact prepare a series of behavioural 'targets' for the young person if, or when, he/she wants to reject adult or parental authority.

Thus, on evidence, from a health point of view, the aim with regard to drinking is different from the aim with regard to smoking. With the latter, the intention is to encourage people to stop, with alcohol it is to produce moderate but controlled drinking. This goes against some cherished adult values which perhaps need reflecting on in the light of what has been said above. And it is interesting to observe that despite a few excesses in drink in teenagers and beyond, the drinking habits of parents are often eventually reverted to.

Tobacco and alcohol are drugs in common use (and smoking is unacceptably high even in twelve and thirteen year olds) and both can be very dangerous in excess to the health of the person using them. Drug abuse, although of course a very serious matter, has to be seen against this background of the easy use of tobacco and alcohol. Many of those addicted to or misusing drugs are young people with a variety of problems, including a history of emotional deprivation, disturbance and separation in the family. The prevalence of drug misuse is not easily assessed but is believed to be considerable. The only accurate figures relating directly to drug misuse are related to notified addicts receiving treatment in hospitals (see *Prevention and Health*). In 1971 the number receiving treatment in Great Britain aged between fifteen and nineteen was under 100 men and about 30 women. In 1977 the figures had dropped to 15 and 10 respectively (see *Social Trends*). These figures are only the tip of an iceberg. The numbers of unnotified narcotic addicts and those who misuse prescribed drugs or others illicitly obtained, such as barbiturates or cannabis, are not known.

Perhaps one way for schools to deal with these drug problems (apart from controlling the availability of drugs) is in the wider context of health education and care. The long-term use of tobacco linked with a variety of heart and lung diseases, including cancers, is a prime issue. The danger of experimenting with drugs for 'kicks', since it can lead to dependence and death, is another. The mistaken belief that there is a 'pill for every ill' is a third. Excess alcohol intake associated with cirrhosis of the liver, chronic malnutrition, brain damage and damage to the foetus, is a fourth. Inappropriate dietary habits, leading to obesity, heart disease and dental caries are a fifth. Inadequate exercise, which is also a risk factor in heart and circulatory disease, is a sixth.

Suicide

Suicide rates in England and Wales in the years 1968-74 for the 10-14 year old group was 1 in 100,000, and suicides are coming forward in age. Every decade shows this (see *Child deaths from accidents and violence*). One suicide represents the tip of the iceberg because for every one death there are probably ten attempts, though it is difficult to assess how many of these were intended to succeed; many of them are probably cries for help. The causes of suicide tend to be basically social in nature and related to stresses in the family (rising divorce rates and the break-up of the nuclear family) the school, the peer group or society. Adolescence is a time of physical growth and emotional and social development. It is also a time when a child changes from primary to secondary school, when examinations take place and when jobs have to be obtained. All these times are stressful and have been associated with attempted and successful suicides. The pastoral care system of schools and the sensitivity of their 'early warning systems' for pupils who might be at risk are, of course, very important. So is a school which views adolescents with kindness, however difficult they are. Good pupil-teacher relationships are involved, so that a boy or girl in difficulties can talk about them to at least one person whom he or she trusts.

Violent and disruptive behaviour

Although opinions vary as to which age group poses the worst problem, fourteen to sixteen are the ages at which violent and disruptive behaviour, including fighting, bullying, assault, loud and aggressive behaviour, are at their height. Other problems exist at this stage too, such as intimidation and working in protection rackets. Dumb insolence or confrontation with a teacher, swearing, smoking, lateness, truancy, are other common behaviour problems.

Exact record keeping and problems of definition limit the evidence but it is clear that behaviour problems are more common in secondary than in primary schools. They are more common among boys than among girls, in urban than in rural areas and among low ability, disadvantaged pupils. It is important however to keep the incidence of violence in perspective, for only a small proportion of pupils in schools has ever behaved violently, with violent and disruptive behaviour being concentrated in only a few schools. The Secondary Report (and experience) confirms these remarks; that the great majority of schools have no disruptive pupils, about a third have some and the schools with the heaviest concentrations of problems are to be found in inner-city or less prosperous suburban areas.

A large number of factors appear to be linked with violent and disruptive pupils. It appears that they are of low ability and have a poor self image; there is often a record of violence and criminality in their families. Most are poor, live in inadequate housing and belong to large families. Often parental discipline is inconsistent and for a variety of reasons there is a prolonged absence of the father during a child's adolescence. This set of factors is very similar to those related to criminal behaviour in the young, by Barbara Wootton.[101] She found that the young criminal had often been in trouble at school and played truant there, was often in a dead-end job in an uninspiring district, came from the lower social classes and a broken home. Clearly, from what has been said, the home and family are crucial influences on behaviour but there is little doubt that schools themselves, even in a disadvantaged area, as Michael Rutter writes, can be 'a force for the good'.[102] The work regime of a school can influence violence and disruption, for schools that place too little emphasis on nonacademic achievement and too much on competition have a negative effect on some children, who lose confidence, cannot keep up and drift along at the back of the class, bored and apathetic. Others in these circumstances may react more violently against what school stands for. Michael Rutter and others have tried to tease out what kind of school is a 'force for good' in terms of behaviour in school, delinquency out of school, attendance at school, employment after school and academic attainment. What seems to matter above all else is the ethos of a school, its style and quality of life and especially the way people treat each other within it. If teachers are ready to see children at any time, trust them to look after their own books and folders, display their work on the walls and generally have high expectations of them, then delinquency is less frequent. Equally, if teachers provide positive models and act together as a staff to support policy on curriculum and approaches to discipline, this has a positive effect. In addition, a good academic balance in a school's intake is crucial, for a proportion of intellectually able children raises the performance of others, while a high proportion of less able children in a school is associated with a high propensity to delinquency. While buildings do not matter greatly, a clean, bright and cheerful school where childrens' paintings, models and written work are displayed has a positive effect for good. The Secondary Survey tends to confirm Michael Rutter's observation about balance of intake:

> The presence of as much as 20 per cent of slow learners or a group of disruptive pupils evidently does not automatically plunge a school into difficulties. But there may be a threshold beyond which the proportion of pupils of very limited ability, presenting a variety of learning problems, the number of disturbed and disturbing children, the proportion with troubled home backgrounds, the inadequacy of resources, whether of specialist skills among the staff or in the facilities offered by the buildings, the generally depressing character of the outer environment, may together create problems of a different order. The gulf between that very small minority of schools and the rest is the more marked, given the reassuring — and it is highly reassuring — picture of the great majority of all secondary schools.

Death and bereavement

Sula Wolff describes several cases of bereavements suffered by adolescents and its effect on them (see *Children Under Stress*). Although, as mentioned in Chapter 8, at the age of nine or ten grief reactions of the adult type begin to occur, it seems impossible to generalize about their effects on an adolescent's (or younger child's) behaviour at school. Most seem, at least outwardly, to be glad to be there, to have the support of friends and perhaps the grief and stress is shown at home. If the home is stable and the family is around, then death may be less fraught and stressful. Usually teachers know when a child's parent has died and give support unobtrusively and do not press for work. Sometimes however bereaved families feel stigmatized by others: bereaved children feel ashamed that they have no father and will not mention it at school. Loss of a parent can therefore affect attendance and eventually school progress. A good caring school and a trusted teacher to whom a child can talk if he or she wishes, is what most children and adolescents need: to talk freely if they wish on a subject which sets up barriers of silence — 'Give sorrow words', Shakespeare wrote. Chetan, an Asian girl in the fourth year of a secondary school, writes sensitively about her feelings on the death in hospital of her baby nephew and the need for the release of words (see *Aspects of Secondary Education in England*):

> My fear had gone. I knew this was to happen and no-one could prevent it. This was the end of the fear it seemed a relief but I was still shocked.
>
> The days following his death were like living in solitude. There was just nothing to do. I just cried myself to sleep, there was really no-one I could tell. I felt there was no-one in the house no-one to talk to. I knew I would soon be the same as this was what human beings were like. It had to be like that, human did forget but even so it is still in the mind.

Children in these circumstances need more help than adults but with such help they can rapidly adjust to the new situation.

As *Ten Good Schools* states, the test of a pastoral system of a school is the degree to which each pupil and his circumstances, aspirations and development are well known to at least one teacher and the extent to which such information is readily available and used. From the pupils' point of view, another test of effectiveness is the degree to which they understand a system devised for their benefit and which will give them a sympathetic hearing. If a child becomes aggressive or withdrawn or even anti-social at school because of the death of a loved one, this kind of caring school will help. Many schools are of this kind. But there is real concern in schools about pupils in a state of grief and mourning and many teachers require help from those who have experience on how to cope best.

This chapter has presented a depressing catalogue of problems. A couplet by Hendrick Morsman, a Dutch poet, from his poem 'The Old Man and the Youth', quoted in the WHO pamphlet on *Problems of Children of School Age (14-18 years)*, helps us to see them in perspective and sums up the needs and spirit of adolescents:

Grandly and rousingly, I want to live!-
Do you hear? Father, Mother, World, Graveyard!

Chapter 17
Children with Special Needs

Any simple knowledge of biology, of medicine or of the world is sufficient to make us understand that no human being is like another. Each child is unique from the moment of conception and each has a 'special need', that is a special environment in order to maximize his or her unique potential. The Warnock Report[103] relates this human variety to handicap. It states rightly that there are not simply two types of child, the handicapped and non-handicapped just as there are not tall and short or bright and dull, for the 'complexities of individual needs are far greater than this dichotomy implies'. Moreover, the labelling of a child as 'handicapped' (backward, educationally sub-normal, less able, remedial, slow learner, maladjusted) leads to a self-fulfilling prophecy, and the label sticks. Children who are designated for example 'slow learners' live down to that expectation. The Warnock Report thus recommends that the term 'children with learning difficulties' should be used to describe the spectrum of 'handicap', which of course shades into the range of the normal child and into those who may suffer the 'handicap' of giftedness. The *Warnock Report* and before that, *Education, Health and Behaviour*[104] made the point that one in five children has a handicap, the needs of which should be met at some time in a school course by special educational provision. The family who have a handicapped child with a special need is therefore not an odd family in rare circumstances. Many families have gone through the tragedy, sadness and problems of having a handicapped child in their midst. It is worthy of note that four of the five children with special needs are in ordinary schools, although the Warnock Report makes it clear that the number of such children will vary from area to area and from school to school.

The goals of education

Much has been written on handicap by specialists and it is not the aim of this chapter to describe handicaps in any detail, but rather to emphasize four points. First, that as the Warnock Report states in paragraph 1.4, the goals of education for all children are the same. These are, to enlarge a child's knowledge, experience and imaginative understanding and thus his awareness of moral values and capacity for enjoyment; and to enable him to enter the world, after formal education is completed, to take part in society, to be a responsible contributor to it and to be able to stand on his own feet. For a few, the road towards these twin goals is easy but for most it is rough though possible, and for some it is strewn with the obstacles of handicap of body and mind. In this last case however, progress is possible, though sometimes the steps forward are tiny. A wise remark by the head[105] of a school for maladjusted children is relevant here because it emphasizes the need for good rapport between a teacher and the children so that they feel secure with him before he can be appreciated as a teacher (and this goes for most children). The head said 'our children need two lots of school days, one for growing up and one for learning'. Another, a former head[106] of a large infant school, makes a similar point and one which has wide application:

> From the spontaneous, well-organised, open-minded and generous teacher, something 'rubs-off', no matter how many children have to share her; from a teacher whose heart is not in her job, who is idle, or close-minded, or ill-supported by her head teacher and colleagues, nothing of value can, whether she has a class of fifteen or fifty.

The need for a special environment

Second, the quality of the 'environment' provided for children with learning difficulties, whether these are of vision, hearing, speech or something else (and many handicaps are multiple), depends on their early detection in the pre-school period. If this is achieved so that the essential emotional, social and conceptual experiences which are crucial to sound learning and relationships are understood by the family and the school, then the appropriate environmental experiences to minimize the disability can be provided. The Warnock Report summarizes these as: the need for the provision of special means of access to the curriculum, including special facilities and teaching techniques (the provision of ramps or handrails for a physically handicapped child or techniques for communicating with a profoundly deaf child); next, the need for a special or modified curriculum with specific objectives and not just one providing a 'stimulating environment'. The child with severe learning difficulties (such as one with Down's syndrome) needs a structured individual programme since he is not as skilled as the normal child in communicating his failure to understand.

All these needs require precise diagnosis followed sometimes by the combined efforts of specialist teams. As an example of detailed diagnosis and the design of a special programme with precise aims, the moving case of Ian in *Teaching language and Communication to the Mentally Handicapped*[107] should be read. Ian is a child of fourteen with Down's syndrome and no real language. His teacher's basic aim after assessment was to develop Ian's communication skills in such a way that he pointed to what he wanted. At the end of six months Ian had been taught to communicate in a consistent, positive manner and more than that, he had become more extroverted and lively.

The influence of a 'perceptive' parent on a handicapped child, here a mother with a blind child is profound and an example is given below:[108]

> Bearing in mind the extreme importance in early childhood of visual exploration of the environment clearly it is most important to be able to intervene effectively in the development of blind infants ... the 'better' blind babies were those whose mothers had developed communication with their blind babies through an alternative channel. They read 'signs' from the babies' hands and gave the children feedback through tactile and kinaesthetic channels. This meant the setting up of a kind of dialogue and these children developed intelligence and language more reliably and earlier than the others.

Still on the theme of environmental quality, some of the origins of environmental stresses which interfere with the growth of body, intellect and character as described in earlier chapters lie in neglect by the mother *before* a child is born: many do not bother to keep ante-natal appointments in the early stages of pregnancy or go to the baby clinics after the birth; in addition more 'working-class' mothers smoke in pregnancy and increase the chances of a low birth-weight baby, with the hazards involved. It needs to be stated, however, that some of the origins of abnormality lie in the lottery of the chromosomes and genes and minor neurological abnormalities, and *not* in ineffective parents and broken homes.

A most important role of the teacher in the pre-school years is to recognize a special need in a child. In this respect, Dr Mary Sheridan has[109] stated that 'it is in the nature of a normally developing *body* to be continually active, of a normally developing *mind* to be intensely curious and of a normally developing *personality* to seek friendly relations with people'. Any inactive, incurious, withdrawn or aggressive child may need special help to make sure that he is not sick or has not a special learning difficulty or is not suffering from the effects of a bad home. Obesity, squint, infantile speech (which can persist in four and five year olds and crystalize into permanent speech troubles), hearing difficulties and social disadvantage are all 'handicaps' for which the nursery school teacher or play group teacher should be alert[30]. As Dr Sheridan wisely remarked, a mother's suspicions that a child is not seeing, hearing, moving his limbs or taking notice like other children of his age, are usually the earliest indications that all is not well. The mother is usually right.

Crucial years for learning

Third, this book has stressed the importance to learning of the years from birth to five. During this time, the brain and sense organs are growing fast and a child then is particularly sensitive to experience and language, and quick to learn from it. At the end of its third year a child's brain weighs on average 1115g. By the time it is fully grown, at about twenty, it weighs about 1400g — an addition of 285g; it is worth repeating the fact that the size of the brain is but poorly related to its functional capacity.

Getting parents back into the driving seat

Fourth, those parents who have a seriously handicapped child such as one with spina bifida or Down's syndrome, sometimes wish the child was dead, or want to kill it or reject it. These feelings are natural and if they are shared with parents in similar circumstances they may be helped to come to terms with their circumstances, and in spite of guilt feelings know that they still love the child. Parents too need to be taught the practical skills necessary to help the child so that he can reach his maximum potential. Parents can help each other in this and ten minutes of a mother's time with another in similar circumstances are worth hours of discussion with those less informed. Teaching parents skills by whatever method, is the way to get them back into the driving seat. It is they who have the responsibility from birth to adulthood for the developing child, it is they who are constant and who matter most. Schools and other agencies, though of course helpful, are incidental influences.

Physical and psychological evidence thus reinforces the case that the education of children with disabilities or significant difficulties must begin as early as possible, while the brain is in a formative state; and as the Warnock Report states, in the earliest years, parents rather than teachers should be regarded wherever possible as the main educators of their children. The Warnock Report itself has much practical advice on the way forward for parental help.

Gifted children

No treatment of 'handicap' should ignore the plight of some children who are gifted and may be at risk because of underachievement and maladjustment. The pamphlet, *Gifted Children in Middle and Comprehensive Secondary Schools* makes suggestions about identification and provision for particular aspects of giftedness rather than general giftedness. In the context of 'special need', a gifted child is like any other child. He is an individual with a need which requires diagnosis and provision to maximize his potential. Some are likely to be missed because a school may lack a sound identification procedure for gifted pupils which should be part of a programme of monitoring individual differences throughout the school, and because a gifted child needs to meet with the right individual teacher (in particular at the secondary stage); one who loves his subject and can communicate it with enthusiasm and delight to a pupil who is going to love the same thing. Some teachers have provided the stimulating environment for gifted children who grew up to be famous: Emlyn Williams and Lloyd George to name two. In addition, some gifted children are missed through their own deliberate underachievement. They want to be accepted in their peer group but the fact of being different can create difficulties for them.

A school curriculum which fails to reveal thought processes above average can also mask high ability while a poor pastoral care system, in which a tutor is not able to use all the experience of a child built up by the school to help with parental backing of a gifted child, are other factors that harm success. Indeed a gifted child may be doubly handicapped if the school is failing him and if his home is not interested and does not understand him. Sometimes too a family is hostile to his gifts because he is so arrogant and attempts to cut himself off. A good school, which recognizes individuality and potential and does its best to cater for them, can help in all these circumstances.

Ethnic minority children

It is appropriate to mention in this chapter the special needs of pupils from ethnic minorities. All that can be said here is that they share many of the hopes, experiences and interests of indigenous children but their range of special needs stems from differences in language, culture and background. Some of these children need to learn English but the major need now is for English language teaching among children who, though born in this country, come from homes where English is little used. And of course, their special need as indicated goes beyond language into a curriculum that takes into account their different and rich cultures.

The stress on individual differences in children, their discovery and provision for their special needs is the note on which to end this book. Schools which achieve these goals are numerous because over the past 50 years there has been an ever deepening concern with children as individuals, which has spread from nursery and infant schools to junior schools and to the secondary school. This concern manifests itself in an awareness of the growing child as a whole, with closely woven spiritual, emotional, intellectual and physical needs and in the appreciation of the varied talents and temperaments any one class holds. At secondary level those schools where pastoral and academic systems interlock so that an all round view of the child or young person is gained and built up by good continuity with primary schools are the most successful. But these strengths are magnified if parents are in close partnership with schools. For the parents and family are the most formative influences on a child and next to these, the teacher.

The whole person

In taking into account individual differences, IQ is but one measure.

To put 'IQ' in perspective, however, it is fitting perhaps to end this book with what Binet[110] himself wrote on intelligence tests in the early years of this century, for his words reflect a striking concern for the whole man and not simply with a narrow view of intelligence:

> Our examination of intelligence cannot take account of all those qualities — attention, will, popularity, perseverance, teachableness and courage, which play so important a part in school work, and also in after life; for life is not so much a conflict of intelligences as a struggle between characters.

REFERENCES

1 GREAT BRITAIN. DEPARTMENT OF EDUCATION AND SCIENCE (1978). *Primary Education in England*. London: HMSO.
2 PLOWDEN REPORT. GREAT BRITAIN. DEPARTMENT OF EDUCATION AND SCIENCE. CENTRAL ADVISORY COUNCIL FOR EDUCATION (ENGLAND) (1967). *Children and their Primary Schools*. London: HMSO.
3 GREAT BRITAIN. DEPARTMENT OF EDUCATION AND SCIENCE (1977). 'Ten Good Schools: A Secondary School Enquiry', HMI Series, *Matters for Discussion,* 1. London:HMSO.
4 GREAT BRITAIN. DEPARTMENT OF EDUCATION AND SCIENCE (1979). *Aspects of Secondary Education in England*. London: HMSO.
5 BROWNE, S.J. (1979). Letter, dated 29th November, to Society of Education Officers.
6 DENT, H.C. (1970) 1870-1970: *Century of Growth in English Education*. Longman.
7 HOLMES, E. (1911). *What is and What Might be*. Constable.
8 BOARD OF EDUCATION (1931). *The Primary School*. London: HMSO.
9 *Report of the Inter-Departmental Committee on Physical Deterioration* (1904).
10 COWIE, E.E. (1973). *Education: Examining the Evidence, 19th Century England*. Methuen.
11 OFFICE OF POPULATION CENSUSES AND SURVEYS (1977). 'Child Health', *Spotlight,* 3. London: HMSO.
12 LOWNDES, G.A.N. (1969). *The Silent Social Revolution — An Account of the Expansion of Public Education in England and Wales 1895-1965*. OUP.
13 BRIERLEY, J.K. (1970). *A Natural History of Man*. Heinemann.
14 COURT REPORT. DEPARTMENT OF HEALTH AND SOCIAL SECURITY and DEPARTMENT OF EDUCATION AND SCIENCE (1976). *Fit for the Future*. London: HMSO.
15 ISAACS, S. (1933). *Social development in Young Children: a study of beginnings*. Routledge.
16 HOLT, J. (1969). *How Children Fail*. Penguin.
17 HOLT, J. (1970). *How Children Learn*. Penguin.
18 TINBERGEN, N. (1976). *The Importance of Being Playful*. BAECE.
19 BRIERLEY, J.K. (1967). *Biology and the Social Crisis*. Heinemann.
20 PENROSE, L.S. (1963). *Outline of Human Genetics*. Heinemann.
21 BRUNER, J.S. (1960). *Towards a Theory of Instruction*. Harvard.
22 OPCS MONITOR (1974). *Congenital Malformations*. London: HMSO.
23 GREAT BRITAIN. DEPARTMENT OF HEALTH AND SOCIAL SECURITY and DEPARTMENT OF EDUCATION AND SCIENCE (1977). *Prevention and Health*. London: HMSO.
24 BRIERLEY, J.K. (1973). *The Thinking Machine*. Heinemann.
25 POLANI, P.E. (1967). Chromosome anomalies and the brain, Guys Hospital Reports, **116.**
26 YOUNG, J.Z. (1971). *An Introduction to the Study of Man*. Oxford.

27 DAVIES, R., BUTLER, N. and GOLDSTEIN, H. (1972). *From Birth to Seven.* Second Report of the National Child Development Study. Longman.
28 GILLIE, O. and MERCER, D. (1978). *The Sunday Times Book of Body Maintenance.* Michael Joseph.
29 DRYDEN, R. (1978). *Before Birth.* Heinemann.
30 BUTLER, N. (July 1972). 'The Shrinking World of Childhood', *Maternal and Child Care.*
31 TANNER, J.M. (1978). *Foetus into Man.* Open Books.
32 BRIERLEY, J.K. (1976). *The Growing Brain.* NFER.
33 YOUNG, J.Z. (1978). *Programs of the Brain.* Oxford.
34 TANNER, J.M. (1978). *Education and Physical Growth.* ULP.
35 DONALDSON, M. (1978). *Children's Minds.* Fontana.
36 GOODNOW, J. (1977). *Children's Drawing.* Fontana/Open Books.
37 PENFIELD, W. (1975). *The Mystery of the Mind.* Princeton.
38 BRIERLEY, J.K. (1978). *Growing and Learning.* Ward Lock.
39 WHITEHEAD, A.N. (1932). *The Aims of Education.* Williams & Norgate.
40 PIAGET, J. (1977). *The Moral Judgement of the Child.* Penguin.
41 WOLFF, S. (1969). *Children Under Stress.* Allen Lane.
42 BLACK, D. (1979). 'Counselling bereaved children and their families', *J. Inst. Health Educ.,* **II.**
43 HILDEBRAND, J. (1979). 'Counselling bereaved families'. *Counselling News,* 29, British Association for Counselling.
44 ELLIOTT, H.C. (1970). *The Shape of Intelligence.* Allen and Unwin.
45 CAMPBELL, F. (1978). 'Preliminary results of as physiologically based treatment of amblyopia', *Br. J. Opthalmology,* **II,** 62.
46 PENFIELD, W. and ROBERTS, L. (1959). *Speech and Brain Mechanisms.* Oxford.
47 STERN, D. (1977). *The First Relationship: Infant and Mother.* Fontana/Open Books.
48 CLARKE, A.M. and CLARKE, A.D.B. (1978). *Early Experience: Myth and Evidence.* Open Books.
49 KAGAN, J. (1979). *The Growth of the Child.* Harvester Press.
50 FRANKLIN, V. *et al.* (Jan. 1974). 'The Development of Language in Genie: a case of language acquisition beyond the critical period', *Brain and Language,* **1,** 1, 81-107.
51 JESPERSON, O. (1922). *Language, its Nature, Development and Origin.* Allen and Unwin.
52 BRIERLEY, J.K. (Spring 1975). 'The Young Brain and Language', *The Use of English.*
53 MILLER, G.A. (1972). *'Linguistic Communication as a Biological Process.'* In: *Biology and the Human Sciences.* Oxford.
54 PFEIFFER, J.E. (1969). *The Emergence of Man.* Harper & Row.
55 DARWIN, C. (1872). *The Expression of the Emotions in Man and Animals.* London.
56 HUGHES, M. and PINKERTON, G. (23rd October 1979). 'Taking a little trouble at the start', *Education Guardian.*

57 OPIE, I. and OPIE, P. (1976).In: BRUNER, J.S. *et. al. Play: its role in development and evolution.* Penguin.
58 MONTESSORI, M. (1936). *The Secrets of Childhood.* Longmans.
59 TINBERGEN, N. (1972). 'Functional ethology and the human sciences', *Proc. Roy. Soc.,* B, 182.
60 CHUKOVSKY, K. (1976). In: BRUNER, J.S. *et al. Play: its role in development and evolution.* Penguin.
61 BRYANT, P. (1974). *Perception and Understanding in Young Children.* Methuen.
62 TAYLOR, G.R. (1979). *The Natural History of the Mind.* Secker & Warburg.
63 BRUNER, J. (1960). *The Process of Education.* Harvard.
64 BOWLBY, J. (1979). *Separation, Anxiety and Anger.* Hogarth.
65 FOLKHARD, S. (1980). 'A note on time and day effects in school children's immediate and developed recall of meaningful material — the influence of the importance of the information tested', *Br. J. Psychology.*
66 MACFARLANE, A. (1979). 'Child deaths from accidents: place of accident', *Population Trends,* 13.
67 (29th November 1975). 'Childhood Poisoning: prevention and management', *Br. Med. J.,* **4,** 5995, 483-4.
68 OPIE, I. and OPIE, P. (1951). *Oxford Dictionary of Nursery Rhymes.* Oxford.
69 MACFARLANE, A. (1978). 'Child deaths from accidents and violence', *Population Trends,* 12.
70 OPCS MONITOR (17th July 1979). 'Deaths from Accidents and Violence'.
71 SANDELS, S. (1968). *Children in Traffic.* Elek.
72 GREAT BRITAIN. CSO (1979). *Social Trends.* London: HMSO.
73 NATIONAL CHILDREN'S BUREAU (October 1977). 'Children's Housing', *Highlight,* 31.
74 ILLINGWORTH, C. *et al.* (8th November 1975). '200 injuries caused by playground equipment', *Br. Med. J.*
75 JACKSON, R.H. and WILKINSON, A.W. (22nd May 1976). 'Why don't we prevent childhood accidents', *Br. Med. J.*
76 DICKERSON, J.W.T. (1979). 'Midday Meals at School', *Daily Telegraph,* Letters.
77 DEPARTMENT OF EDUCATION AND SCIENCE (1975). *Nutrition in Schools.* Working Party Report on Nutritional Aspects of School Meals. London: HMSO.
78 DEPARTMENT OF EDUCATION AND SCIENCE (1971). *Slow Learners in Secondary Schools.* London: HMSO.
79 DEPARTMENT OF HEALTH AND SOCIAL SECURITY (1980). *Lead and Health.* London: HMSO.
80 GAINSBURG, H. (1972). *The Myth of the Deprived Child.* Prentice Hall.
81 NATIONAL CHILDREN'S BUREAU (1976). 'The Father's Role', *Highlight,* 24.
82 FALKNER, F. and TANNER, J.M. (1979). *Human Growth.* (3 vols.). Plenum. (See esp. chaps. by BROOK, C.G.D., MARSHALL, W.A., WINTER, J.S.D., RABINOWICZ, T., SCOTT, J.P.).
83 BROOK, C.G.D. (1973). 'Obesity in Children'. *Nursing Mirror,* **137,** 3, 40-2.

84 WEST, R.J. and LLOYD, J. (October 1976). 'Coronary heart disease', *Roy. Soc. Health J.*

85 DEPARTMENT OF EDUCATION AND SCIENCE (1963). *Half our Future.* London: HMSO. (Newsom Report).

86 MORAN, P. (April 1978). 'A visitor's perspective'. In: *Education 3-13,* **6,** 1.

87 COLTHAM, J.B. (April 1978). 'Middle Years without Middle Schools'. In: *Education 3-13,* **6,** 1.

88 DEPARTMENT OF EDUCATION AND SCIENCE (1978). *Truancy and Behavioural Problems in Some Urban Schools.* London: HMSO.

89 PRINCE, S. (25th June 1973). 'Adolescent stress in the home', *Med. News.*

90 LAUFER, M. (1975). *Adolescent Breakdown and Disturbance.* Pelican.

91 DEPARTMENT OF EDUCATION AND SCIENCE (1977). *Gifted Children in Middle and Comprehensive Secondary Schools.* HMI Series, Matters for Discussion 4: London: HMSO.

92 DEPARTMENT OF EDUCATION AND SCIENCE, CLEGG, A. (1970). 'The Achievement of the Education Service 1870-1970'. In:*1870 Education Act,* Commemorative Lectures. London: HMSO.

93 McKEOWN, T. (1976). *The Modern Rise of Population.* Arnold.

94 WORLD HEALTH ORGANIZATION (1975). Problems of Childhood: School age 5-9 years. Copenhagen, ICP/MCN 004; also see School age 14-8.

95 MOTTRAM, V.H. (1972). *Human Nutrition.* Arnold.

96 MORGAN, H.G. (24th December 1977). 'Fasting girls and our attitudes to them', *Br. Med. J.*

97 NATIONAL COUNCIL FOR ONE PARENT FAMILIES (1979). *Pregnant at School.* (Chairperson of working party Dame Margaret Miles.)

98 SCHOFIELD, M. (1973). *The Sexual Behaviour of Young Adults.* Allen Lane.

99 FARRELL, C. (1978). *My mother said . . . the way young people learned about sex and birth control.* Routledge & Kegan Paul.

100 DAVIES, J. and STACEY, B. (1972). *Teenagers and Alcohol: a developmental study in Glasgow.* London: HMSO.

101 WOOTTON, B. (1959). *Social Science and Social Pathology.* Allen and Unwin.

102 RUTTER, M. *et al.* (1979). *Fifteen Thousand Hours: Secondary schools and their effects on Children.* Open Books.

103 WARNOCK REPORT. DEPARTMENT OF EDUCATION AND SCIENCE. (1978). *Special Educational Needs.* Report of the Committee of Enquiry into the Education of Handicapped Children and Young People. London: HMSO.

104 RUTTER, M., TIZARD, J. and WHITMORE, K. (1970). *Education, Health Behaviour.* Longman.

105 LANSDOWN, R. (1970). *Day Schools for Maladjusted Children.* Association of Workers for Maladjusted Children.

106 WEBB, L. (1967). *Children with Special Needs in the Infant School.* Colin Smythe.

107 LEEMING, K. *et al.* (1979). *Teaching Language and Communications to the Mentally Handicapped.* Schools Council Curriculum Bulletin, 8. Evans/Methuen Educational.

108 EVANS, D. (1979). 'Some recent research in the development of very young children and some possible implications for remedial education', *Links*.

109 SHERIDAN, M. (1973). *Children's Developmental Progress from Birth to five years: the Stycar sequences*. NFER.

110 BINET, A. (1908). 'L'annee psychologique', quoted in HADOW REPORT (1924). London: HMSO.

Index